Edited by Caitlin DeSilvey, Simon Naylor & Colin Sackett

Anticipatory history

Uniformbooks 2011

First published 2011
Copyright © University of Exeter / Individual contributors, 2011
Supported by the AHRC Landscape and Environment programme

ISBN 978-0-9568559-2-3

Uniformbooks
7 Hillhead Terrace, Axminster, Devon EX13 5JL
www.uniformbooks.co.uk

Printed and bound by R. Booth, Penryn, Cornwall

Stephen Daniels

Foreword

We are ever in need of words to describe the world and express our relations with it. 'Landscape' and 'Environment', the title of the AHRC programme which includes the project that produced this fine volume, are themselves such words, framing or shaping our view of the physical and social world and our place in it. They are in Raymond Williams' phrase 'keywords', historically and geographically complex concepts, words with their own situated stories, literary as well as linguistic. Here are words that emerge, expand, enclose, erode and re-emerge, not less than the physical and social worlds they describe; their semantic fields describe territories of contested meaning as well as arenas of common ground. Landscape and environment are connected to wider worlds of word making, other concepts like place, nature, site, scenery, and more specialist terms like living landscapes or environmental art.

Reflecting the wide-ranging community, and their domains of know-ledge, which the project brought together, and their conversations and exchanges at particular moments, the words of this book—old, new, public and professional—range widely, mostly to describe processes at various temporal and spatial scales and unfold stories of environmental change. Some words like woods and commons are familiar and seem stable but are revealed as dynamic, disputed and geographically specific; some are technical terms like equilibrium and cycle of erosion, if defined in unexpected ways. Concepts of coastal squeeze and managed realignment have a particular purchase on the regional setting of this project, as do moor and rhododendron. New coinages like story-radar, palliative curation and the project's own major 'conceptual tool' anticipatory history, have the metaphorical capacity to creatively refigure the way we imagine the world and intervene—or not—in its workings. These words, and the various meanings which are explored in the entries on them, resonate well beyond the world of this project. They display the range of knowledge and depth of feeling about landscape matters, of researchers, practitioners, and a wider public. They encourage people to put into words concerns about landscape change that are so often difficult to precisely express.

Stephen Daniels is Professor of Cultural Geography, University of Nottingham and Director of the AHRC's Landscape and Environment programme

Contents

Introduction   9

Acclimatisation   21   Longue durée   45
Adaptation   22   Managed realignment   46
Art   23   Memory   46
Aspic   24   Monitoring   47
Besanded   25   Moor   48
Birds   26   Museum   49
Catastrophe   27   Natural history   51
Coastal squeeze   27   Natural selection   53
Collection   29   Nature writing   53
Commons   30   Palliative curation   56
Continuities   31   Place   57
Cycle of erosion   32   Presentism   57
Discontinuity   33   Record   58
Dream-map   34   Recording   59
Ebb and flood   35   Rewilding   61
Enclosure   35   Rhododendron   62
Entropy   37   Sculpture trail   63
Epiphany   37   Shifting baseline syndrome 64
Equilibrium   38   Story-radar   66
Erosion   39   Temprocentrism   67
Extinction   40   Tides   67
Futurology   42   Uncertainty   69
Introductions   42   Unfarming   69
Liminal zone   43   Woods   70
Living landscapes   44   Zone of exclusion   71

Place index   72
Contributors   75
Acknowledgements   77

Anticipatory history

Reports of accelerating sea level rise, species extinction, shifting weather patterns, stressed landscapes, and coastal erosion—such material is the daily fare of a twenty-first century media diet. We are told that we are facing the real prospect of an increase in the rate and scale of environmental change in our lifetimes. Many of these changes—if predictions are correct—will register as subtle (or not so subtle) alterations in familiar landscapes: a lost section of coastal path, a favourite flower vanished, dwindling populations of waterbirds in a local saltmarsh, the removal of a customary fishing quay.[1] But the range of available responses to these changes is limited—usually cast in terms of loss and guilt—and we often do not have the cultural resources to respond thoughtfully, to imagine our own futures in a tangibly altered world.

From September 2010 to April 2011 we gathered people in a research network to explore the roles that history and story-telling play in helping us to apprehend and respond to changing landscapes, and to changes to the wildlife and plant populations they support. This might seem a surprising place to begin an investigation into the potential consequences of environmental change. It is more common to think in scientific or policy terms when dealing with these matters. However, our argument is that the humanities have much to contribute to these debates. In a recent interview, historian Hayden White proposed the concept of a 'progressive history'. Progressive history is guided by a concern for the future, and looks to the past to find intellectual, emotional, and spiritual resources to help us direct this concern towards sustaining specific communities—both human and ecological. White commented:

> We study the past not in order to find out what really happened there or to provide a genealogy of and thereby a legitimacy for the present, but to find out what it takes to face a future we should like to inherit rather than one that we have been forced to endure.[2]

Something of this intention guided the conversations we had during our various network workshops. We framed our network around the concept of 'anticipatory history'—a historiographical position that shares the future orientation of White's progressive history, but is perhaps more modest and less moralistic in emphasis.[3] The term itself is adapted from the concept of 'anticipatory adaptation', which is used in discussion of climate change to describe action taken before impacts are felt, as distinguished from 'passive' or 'reactive' adaptation strategies. Practitioners of anticipatory adaptation strategies seek to identify vulnerable places or populations, and then weigh up the costs and benefits of different adaptive interventions, with a focus on 'no regret' measures that will provide benefits even if the predicted change is never realised.[4] Although supportive of this principle, it was our feeling that such work would benefit from looking back as much as gazing only forward; that in a variety of ways the past has much to contribute to our preparations for the future. This might include using archives of environmental change to appreciate or re-interpret present circumstances; or even the production of experimental accounts of historic environmental processes to help us apprehend future paths and opportunities.

Our conversations sometimes revealed fault lines, one in particular around the practice of intentional, or even instrumental, history-writing. Some at the table had a lingering discomfort with the idea of making historical narrative do certain kinds of social and cultural 'work'.[5] The term 'revisionist history' carries negative connotations, implying the deliberate distortion of historical data to serve contemporary interests, politically motivated or otherwise. It is often associated with the exercise of power— the production of 'future histories' that establish a narrative trajectory based on a selective reading of the past, and then project this into the formation of a desired prospective landscape.[6] We have focused instead on what we began to think of as *re-vision*-ist history—the opportunity to change the way we *envision* the past in place. We have been exploring the idea that this kind of work is particularly salient in relation to changing ecologies and landscapes.

Background assumptions about succession and stability (in animal and plant populations) and conservation and constancy (in landscapes, particularly those we value) often obscure the dynamism that shaped these places and their inhabitants. Species loss, erosion, accretion, and climate change are part of the past in these places, not just part of their future. History that calls attention to process rather than permanence may therefore help us to be more prepared for future change; to respond thoughtfully and proactively, rather than in a mode of retreat and or regret.[7] As historian William Cronon notes in his essay 'Why the Past Matters': "[O]ur ability to project ourselves into the future, imagining alternative lives that lead us to set new goals and work toward new ends, is merely the forward expression of the experience of change we have learned from reflecting on the past."[8] This is not then an activity in nostalgia, which begins by assuming its job is to highlight and lament decline or loss over time. It is also not necessarily anti-managerial. Indeed, it is often pragmatic calculations that drive the need for a historiographical or philosophical shift in thinking in the first place.

This network has been actively exploring the implications of this kind of thinking by bringing together academics and practitioners to talk about how the stories we tell about ecological and landscape histories shape our perception of what we might call future 'plausabilities'. Our exchanges wove together theory and practice, representation and interpretation, experimentation and application. We asked how past, present and prospective changes are constructed and communicated, but we were also interested in discussing how we might engage with these narrative processes. In the following section we provide some examples of how anticipatory history thinking may apply in different contexts, and intersect with other areas of concern—including the communication of science, the pragmatics of land management and the practice of art. We hope that this brief elaboration will help anchor the contributions in the rest of the book, which deal with these issues but often in more specific ways.

Grounding theory
One of the areas where anticipatory history thinking may offer useful perspectives is in reflection on the communication of scientific information. Science has provided us with a fairly consistent language with which to trace changes in nature, such that observations made several hundred years ago can still be referred to today, whether in terms of rainfall, temperature, flood events, alteration of topography, or changes to plant and animal populations. Study of past records remains a cornerstone of much environmental science, will underpin many attempts to calculate future changes and will support any narratives about what is happening in nature. Exactly how these records will serve these functions is not fixed or predictable however. A useful example is that of the Perennial centaury (*Centaurium scilloides*), a plant last seen in the county of Cornwall in the 1960s and assumed to be extinct there. (Its only other known UK habitat is the coast of Pembrokeshire National Park, Wales.) In 2010 a local couple discovered the rare plants growing on coastal cliffs near Gwennap Head, and reported their discovery to the Botanical Society of the British Isles. This record of a 're-found species' shifted the narrative around the Perennial centaury from extinction to possible re-population. Perhaps

their sudden re-emergence was an effect of recent climatic change? Or maybe the plants were there all along and had simply not been spotted and identified, which raises questions about the ability of monitoring methods to effectively account for a region's nature. Was this re-found species ever really lost?

The 're-finding' of the Perennial centaury also connected it into justifications for particular management regimes. Science is often intimately enrolled (albeit reluctantly at times) in such regimes, and is far from a passive provider of objective information. This of course can be controversial and can bring science into conflict with other ways of understanding and appreciating nature. Other times the relationship is more symbiotic. For instance, Peter Bowden, Natural England's Land Management team leader in Cornwall was quoted as saying:

> The Perennial centaury appears to favour cliff-top grassland and maritime heath, exactly the sorts of habitat that we are trying to encourage through our Environmental Stewardship funding in West Penwith. We think the management here, particularly the re-introduction of grazing on the cliffs, has helped to maintain open conditions in an area that would otherwise be liable to encroachment by scrub and bracken. This has not only benefited the Perennial centaury but also a wide range of other wildlife.[9]

One other example cited in our workshops was that of the decision to eradicate two species of rat (the brown rat, *Rattus norvegicus*; and the black rat, *Rattus rattus*) on Lundy Island so as to restore breeding seabird populations, particularly the Manx shearwater and the Atlantic puffin. The Seabird Recovery Project Partnership (which included the National Trust, the Landmark Trust, the RSPB, and English Nature) implemented a cull from 2003 to 2006, which was justified on scientific grounds and did not involve a public consultation. Although it was declared a success, with a return of the shearwaters and puffins to breed,[10] there was an outcry from a number of animal welfare groups, with protests to save the Lundy rats taking place at Bideford Quay and outside the RSPB and Natural England offices in Exeter. Terms like 'slaughter' were used to describe the cull. The risk to other animals from possible ingestion of the poisons was highlighted. Protestors also noted that the rats had been on the island for over 400 years, and in doing so questioned the implication that the rats were recent interlopers—unwanted immigrants that disrupted a settled indigenous nature on the island.

In our discussions it was suggested that there needed to be more sensitivity with regard to the way arguments based solely on scientific facts and reasons were received, and perhaps even the incorporation of a range of other factors in decision-making processes. We might go even further and follow the argument of the biogeographer Steve Trudgill, who urges scientists like himself to acknowledge the moral and even aesthetic bases upon which environmental science sits: "Science can never be value free", Trudgill asserts, and so "ecosystem science should recognize its values and make them explicit and defensible in relation to their emotive and normative content".[11] He goes on to note that motivation to act relies on these responses and that empowering such feelings and "exploring shared personal values enhances the democratization of the conservation debate in such a way that both ecosystem scientists and the public can take part".[12] Here the Lundy rat example is a good one, where justification of the cull rested on a set of moral decisions: that introduced species should be removed to support indigenous species; that less charismatic animals should make way for more popular ones; and that people's emotional responses to the killing of the rats were not relevant to the decision-making process.

Shared exploration of values, such as that advocated by Trudgill, can also take place obliquely, through forums that encourage people to share their diverse understandings of landscape history. If people can be engaged early on (before difficult management decisions have to be taken), a conversation about the different versions of the past that people privilege and promote may help identify and anticipate potential conflict before it comes to a head. Such an application of anticipatory history thinking may be particularly relevant in situations where the prospect of environmental change is forcing a shift in management priorities.

To illustrate this point we travel back to West Penwith, a densely layered landscape of ancient field systems, Bronze Age barrows, Iron Age roundhouses, Neolithic tor enclosures, and the contemporary traces of tourism and agriculture. During our second workshop we heard from National Trust staff about the conflict generated by proposals for re-introduction of grazing on areas of heath and moorland overgrown with bracken and gorse scrub. To summarise a complex story, land managers sought to encourage biodiversity by returning to an era of hands-on management and, in their words, 'reconnecting with the historic uses of landscape'.[13] The plans involved the introduction of cattle grids, and some limited fencing on areas of the moor. They initiated the scheme after an extended public consultation, and were shocked when a vocal and vociferous 'opposition' group formed to campaign against the grazing scheme. The 'Save Penwith Moors' group argued that the developments would disturb the 'wild' character of the moors: "These areas… create a spiritual connection with the numerous prehistoric sacred sites and natural granite outcrops that dot this ancient landscape… Their enclosure will be a disaster not easily undone".[14]

Looking southwest from the base of Carn Galva to Rosemergy Engine House, c.1950; rephotograph, 2011.

There were other issues bound up in this conflict, of course, but the intense disagreement over the future of this landscape makes more sense when we try to understand the different versions of the place's past that were being mobilised in the debate. Natural England and the National Trust stated their intention to reconnect with the historic uses of the landscape, but came to be seen by some as privileging certain historic uses (most notably grazing) and historic ecological conditions in order to support their conservation goals. Arguments that grazing had been carried out on the moor for centuries, and that stock boundaries constructed of traditional materials were key elements in the historic landscape, failed to convince people whose preferred history traced back to a state of untended, undomesticated 'wilderness'. Each group grounded their position in a different understanding of the place's past.

The story of this conflict perhaps highlights an opportunity to make these 'uses' of the past more transparent and participatory. Conversations about landscape history can be used to open up negotiation about landscape futures, flushing out potential points of conflict or disagreement before debates become calcified and contentious. The challenge here is to bring the right people to the table early enough for these conversations to make a difference. One tool to draw people in might be the practice of rephotography, which can make environmental change visible and help people understand that a landscape that seems timeless (and wild, in this case) is actually a very recent artefact. A comparison of two photos taken from the same location at the base of Carn Galva (opposite) shows that densities of gorse scrub and bracken have increased substantially over the past sixty years.[15] Environmental change is often too gradual to register in people's consciousness, but photographs can make this change visible and help people explore 'past scenarios' as a way of opening up conversations about 'future prospects'.[16]

The stories above—about rats and flowers, cows and moors—highlight a key theme that emerged from our workshops. Those who make decisions about landscape futures need to be sensitive to how people know the past in place—the dense weave of individual memories, shared experiences, and personally significant landmarks that makes up our understanding of where we are, and where we have been. Anticipatory history may be capable of tapping into these meanings, in that it does not attempt to construct a singular, authoritative historical narrative. As an approach, it leaves room for expressing the 'small stories' and 'lay knowledges' that are layered in place, and then linking these to a hoped-for future.[17] At the time of writing, Cornwall Wildlife Trust is trying to do just this, again in West Penwith. Its aim is to construct a 'living landscape' of inter-connected wildlife-rich areas that stretches from one coast to the other and covers a working agricultural environment. What is notable about this project is its policy of engaging with various groups about their memories and narratives of place, as much as their land management practices.

In recording and acknowledging these intimate attachments to place, there is a clear role for the creative arts. Music, visual arts practice, and performance may be better able to reflect, and respect, emotional and embodied connections to lived landscapes than text-based narrative forms. A project carried out on the eroding Seven Sisters cliffs in East Sussex provides a potential model for such engagement. In 2005 Red Earth Environmental Art Group choreographed a three-part 'landscape performance' with participation from local communities.[18] In 'Trace' participants created an 'erosion line' across the beach, using white stones to trace the outline of where the base of the cliff face stood 50 years earlier. 'Vanishing point', a temporary sculpture made from greenwood and chalk daub and sited on the cliff-top horizon west of Birling Gap, called attention to the archaeological and geological history of the landscape. 'Journey', the final event, brought together performers and participants to mark the future erosion line on the cliff-top in a procession of white flags. Such site-specific anticipatory art practice holds landscape past and landscape future in productive and provocative tension.

About this book

Clearly there is a place for anticipatory history thinking on different registers and in different contexts. In academic spheres, anticipatory history might contribute to the crafting of new research approaches, and new narrative strategies, that are both more relevant and more rewarding; work that moves into the world, and, in a small way, helps make it. In an applied sense, it can help us to reflect on current practices and share approaches that allow us to 'look back to look forward'. National Trust staff have commented that anticipatory history can work as a 'conceptual tool' for shifting expectations and guiding different—perhaps more open—forms of engagement between people and place, past and future. Others have suggested that anticipatory histories may help make possible the transition from 'incremental' to 'transformational' adaptation—a shift from changing what one *does* to changing what one is trying to *achieve*.[19] Anticipatory history is an idea that is already being put into practice in all sorts of ways. There is an opportunity to name this work, and call attention to it. That is what this book aims to do.

The remainder of this book is made up of a series of entries that in some way have a bearing on anticipatory history. It is designed to function as a glossary or work of reference for anyone wanting to learn more. Over the course of four meetings a number of people participated in an extended discussion about the meaning and efficacy of anticipatory history as a concept and a mode of engagement with the past. As we followed debates we noted down key terms on index cards—words or phrases that have a bearing on aspects of environmental change over time and in place, and our responses to these changes. We then went through a process of culling entries and drafting collective definitions. Lastly, participants were asked to adopt particular key terms and to produce entries. This book is then a work of many hands and can in no way claim to be the product of a single vision. It was never our intention to provide a definitive statement on the means and ends of anticipatory history, even if that was possible to do. In fact our editorial policy was to be as light-touch as possible. The only real restriction placed on contributors was to be broadly sympathetic to the collective ideas put forward by the group. The reader will therefore find entries that differ markedly in length, use of imagery, style and content. Some are very personal, others pretend to be conclusive; some are no more than a few lines, others are the length of short essays; some are purely textual, others are predominantly visual. Perhaps the most important outcome of this editorial policy is the absence of a unifying perspective on the term in question. There will inevitably be some tensions across the entries, not to mention a few contradictions and even disagreements. The format that we have chosen makes room for the peaceful coexistence of different positions, both philosophical and pragmatic. We hope that the reader will not view this as undermining of the venture as a whole; rather we encourage them to take seriously and reflect on the variety of approaches and positions that might be taken when we try to envision our collective environmental futures in place.

How to engage with this book? To borrow from a similar sort of publication, *Patterned Ground*, we can recommend several reading tactics.[20] The first is to read it from beginning to end. The advantage of this approach is that it juxtaposes otherwise disjunct entries and may well trigger interesting resonances or even dissonances. Alternatively, you can make use of the list of entries and jump on to particular words that appeal to you. We have employed a cross-referencing system, so that you can then skip to other related words and move around the book in that way. We have also compiled a place index, which you will find at the end of the book. The reader may like to read the book as a travelogue of the term anticipatory history. How about a journey along the south English coast, from Mullion in Cornwall all the way to Birling Gap in East Sussex? Or from Formby, on the Irish Sea, to the Fens, on the North Sea? There is also an index of contributors, so it is possible to trace who has written what and to consider how topics have been approached from different perspectives and in different voices.

References

1. Natural England, Lost life: England's lost and threatened species (2010), www.naturalengland.org.uk/publications

2. E. Domanska, A conversation with Hayden White, *Rethinking History* 12 (2008) 3–21.

3. The concept of anticipatory history developed out of a research project (funded by the RGS-IBG and the EPSRC) on the National Trust's management of changing coastal landscapes, with a focus on Mullion Harbour, Cornwall. See C. DeSilvey, Making sense of transience: an anticipatory history, *Cultural Geographies*, Special Issue on Narrating Landscape and Environment 19 (2012).

4. J. B. Smith, S. E. Ragland and G. J. Pitss, A process for evaluating anticipatory adaptation measures for climate change, *Water, Air, and Soil Pollution* 92 (1996) 229–238.

5. P. L. Price, Cultural geography and the stories we tell ourselves, *Cultural Geographies* 17 (2010) 203–10.

6. D. Mercer, Future-histories of Hanford: the material and semiotic production of a landscape, *Cultural Geographies* 9 (2002) 35–67.

7. B. Anderson, Preemption, precaution, preparedness: anticipatory action and future geographies, *Progress in Human Geography* 34 (2010) 777–798.

8. W. Cronon, Why the Past Matters, *Wisconsin Magazine of History*, 84 (2000) 2–13.

9. Anon, 'Extinct' plant rediscovered on cliffs near Land's End, Natural England website, http://www.naturalengland.org.uk/regions/south_west/press_releases/2010/240810.aspx, 24 August 2010.

10. J. Lock, Eradication of brown rats *Rattus norvegicus* and black rats *Rattus rattus* to restore breeding seabird populations on Lundy Island, Devon, England, *Conservation Evidence* 3 (2006) 111–113.

11. S. Trudgill, Psychobiogeography: meanings of nature and motivations for a democratized conservation ethic, *Journal of Biogeography* 28 (2001) 677–698, 677.

12. Ibid., 678. See also S. Trudgill, A requiem for the British flora? Emotional biogeographies and environmental change, *Area* 40 (2008) 99–107.

13. Jon Brookes, paper delivered at Anticipatory Histories of Landscape and Wildlife: Workshop 2, 16 December 2010.

14. Ian McNeil Cooke, quoted in A. Pitt, Conservation: running the wilds, *Guardian* 17 September 2008.

15. Jon Brookes presented this comparative example at our December 2010 workshop.

16. S. Daniels and G. Endfield, Narratives of climate change, *Journal of Historical Geography* 35 (2009) 215–222.

17. H. Lorimer, Telling small stories: spaces of knowledge and the practice of geography, *Transactions of the Institute of British Geographers* 28 (2003) 197–217; C. Brace and H. Geoghegan, Human geographies of climate change: Landscape, temporality, and lay knowledges, *Progress in Human Geography* 35 (2011) 284–302.

18. O. Lowenstein, Land, sea and sky: Red Earth's Seven Sisters ritual performance, *Fourth Door Review*, December 2005.

19. Comment from Chris West, Director UKCIP, pers. comm. 27 June 2011.

20. S. Harrison, S. Pile and N. Thrift (Eds) *Patterned Ground: Entanglements of Nature and Culture* (London, Reaktion Books, 2004) 44.

Acclimatisation

The process by which an organism adjusts to a gradual change in its environment. Organisms changing their substance and/or habits to allow them to function as the heat of summer gives way to the cold of winter are said to be undergoing the process of acclimatisation. The capacity to acclimatise has been demonstrated in numerous species and may involve biochemical and morphological changes such as the changing of skin colour or pattern. In some cases, acclimatisation has been observed to be anticipatory in nature, with the process beginning before the change in environment occurs.

Today the term is mainly used to refer to the process of human adjustment to high altitude, but acclimatisation can also be used to describe the adjustments that a person makes in response to urban, social, or political conditions (i.e. acclimatising to life in Cornwall), or the adaptation of plants to cultivation or of animals to captivity.

The words 'acclimatation' and 'acclimation' entered the English language around 1820 from France, where they had been associated with efforts to cultivate exotic plants and breed merino sheep. In the nineteenth century, acclimatisation became a scientific concept, generally referring to an intentional and scientifically-mediated transplantation of organisms (whether human, animal or plant) to new regions. Often used interchangeably with 'naturalisation' or 'domestication', in the human case acclimatisation

'Chinchona-plants at Ootacamund, in August 1861.'

signalled the capacity for adjustment, and was said to be preceded by a process of 'seasoning'. The 'problem' of the acclimatisation of the white European to the equatorial tropics (illustrated by high rates of death and disease) held great political significance.

The first Acclimatisation Society was established in Paris in 1854, from where the Society spread quickly around the world, particularly to European colonies in Australasia. Societies were linked with menageries, natural history museums and agricultural and botanical societies, and were most interested in finding commercial products (i.e. sugar, cotton, quinine, rubber, alpacas) and introducing them to new areas of the world. These activities actively reshaped the landscape for commercial gain, but also with aesthetic (targets included English roses, strawberries, and songbirds) and recreational (fish and game birds) intent, to aid both physical and emotional transition to foreign lands. Although numerous acclimatisation projects failed (proving that nature was beyond European control), others were so successful in their new environments that they crowded out native flora and fauna, and became reclassified as pests or, in time, as 'native' species.

See: Adaptation, Introductions, Museum, Natural history, Rhododendron.

Adaptation

Is it any wonder people are confused about natural selection when the term 'adaptation'—a key concept in evolutionary thinking—is used in so many different ways? For an evolutionary biologist an adaptation is a feature or trait that enables an organism to survive and reproduce in its natural environment more successfully than if it did not possess that feature or trait. Adaptations arise through natural or sexual selection. Antlers in male deer are an adaptation (and hence are said to be adaptive) because they give males a better chance of winning contests for females against other antler-less males and leaving more descendants.

However, the term adaptation is used in other contexts. For example, 'adapting to climate change'. This is confusing because here, 'adapting' *can* mean evolving to respond to climate change (as above), but it can also mean coping with climate change (or acclimatising to climate change) with no evolutionary implications whatsoever. Let's spell this out. Many birds time their breeding such that they lay their eggs for hatching to coincide with times when food is most abundant. The cue birds use to time their breeding is day length: laying at a particular day length results in the chicks hatching at the optimal time. This is an adaptation. Laying at any other time, either earlier or later, will result in the chicks hatching when there is less food available. Few adaptations are 'perfect' and individuals vary in what day length they respond to. Climate change has resulted in warmer spring weather, so the peak of food abundance now occurs earlier. An evolutionary adaptation to climate change results from natural selection favouring those individuals that use a different day length to time their breeding. It works like this: birds that start breeding in response to the original day length cue will rear fewer offspring than those that respond to a different day length and breed earlier. This is because the birds breeding earlier will experience a better food supply for their chicks, rear more chicks and leave more descendants—and this is the key point—with the genes for breeding earlier.

Adaptation, in terms of *coping* with climate change implies no natural selection, no change in gene frequencies, no evolutionary response.

A better term is acclimatisation (or acclimate). Use of this would avoid any confusion.

See: Acclimatisation, Birds, Natural selection.

Art

Art is both a thing and process, much defined and much debated. In its broadest sense, it is the process and product of making individual or group creativity intelligible to others in tangible form.

In the context of anticipatory history art is both provocation against and solace towards newly contextualised, and rarely benign, futures. As a discipline that plots routes from past to future through the prism of our current understanding, anticipatory history shares much in common with contemporary art, which has its own research agendas and processes, distinct from, but not always unrelated to, those of science or other academic disciplines.

Chris Drury 'Heart of Reeds', Lewes, East Sussex, 2005– *"This work lives, grows and changes, providing habitat for other species. The shape uses a complex chaos pattern from blood flow in the heart to create the conditions to maximise the biodiversity of a small local nature reserve on a piece of land once used as an industrial railway siding on the edge of town. A work made for small creatures as well as people. You can get up close and see the microcosm, or climb a nearby hill and see it from above and at a distance."*

Landscape change is a subject that concerns many artists: the natural rhythms of time and seasonality can be found in the durational sculptural works of artists such as Andy Goldsworthy and Chris Drury; journeys through landscape are charted by the extensive performance and documentation of Richard Long and Tim Brennan; and the material and political relationship to nature is explored by the installations, events and media works of, among others, Cornelia Parker and Simon Starling. Histories of contemporary art are doubtless being written that uncover how collective anxieties about change in landscape are being expressed by artists today.

Contemporary art offers ways to connect the concerns of anticipatory history to a wider public that reaches beyond the dense data of scientific research and the textual propositions of history and geography. Such artistic expressions may be intellectual, emotional and rigorous, honed by individual experience: but their punch could come through a honeyed scent, a raw texture, a haunting sound, all set in uncommon juxtaposition.

The National Trust has worked with Red Earth (co-directed by Simon Pascoe and Caitlin Easterby) in creating site specific installations and participatory art events that directly engage with narratives of landscape change. In 2005, a programme called Geograph took place at Birling Gap (East Sussex) where the cliff line of fifty years ago was marked by a delicately traced line of chalk pebbles and boulders, while the predicted erosion line twenty years hence was marked by a procession and flags (also discussed p.15). These interventions provide creative markers of dynamic changes within the landscape—and demonstrate how contemporary art practice can articulate them in powerful ways.

See: Collection, Erosion.

Aspic

A savoury meat jelly, composed of and containing meat, fish, game or hard-boiled eggs. In popular (non-culinary) usage 'aspic' is often preceded by 'fixed in' or 'set in', as in Peter Mandelson's comment that UK academics "think they have a right to be set in aspic in what they do" (11 February 2010). The term frequently appears in reference to the attempted 'preservation' of objects and landscapes in a static and unchanging state, in statements such as this recent Plymouth City Council comment: "We cannot preserve the city centre in aspic and need flexibility to enable the centre to fulfil its role as a lynch pin to the local economy"(BBC, 8 June 2011). 'In aspic' preservation is commonly contrasted with 'conservation'. Conservation, according to the definition proposed by Holland and Rawles in a 1996 report for the Welsh Countryside Council, accepts the inevitability of change and focuses on "negotiating the transition from past to future in such a way as to secure the transfer of maximum significance".

The above is an attempt at the disambiguation of 'aspic'. It helps, up to a point, but also introduces some elements of reambiguation. The extraction of cartilaginous gelatine from joints of meat for use in setting a mould around perishable delicacies developed in the eighteenth century; this method of presentation had the added benefit of slowing the spoilage of the suspended food products, as the jelly acted as a barrier to the ingress of air and bacteria. A thin glaze of aspic was sometimes used to present food for display. I have not been able to track down the first time the aspic metaphor was applied to a building, or a landscape. We could speculate that John Ruskin, suffering from a bout of indigestion after an aspic-heavy meal, coined the usage. The odd thing is that it stuck, despite its imprecision. Foodstuffs 'set in aspic' still decay, just more slowly. By extension, we would suppose that a building (or an academic) set in aspic is only temporarily protected from agents of decomposition and change, and when the end comes it is, presumably, quite messy.

Perhaps this is just a reminder that many of the words we use to describe our world have similarly incongruous applications. The words 'conservation' and 'preservation', on the face of it so neutral and straightforward, have their own tangled genealogies. The terms are often used interchangeably, but they have very different connotations depending on whether they are applied to 'natural' or 'cultural' objects, and, to some extent, where the speaker lives. To make a crude comparison, the term 'conservation' is more often applied to plants, animals, and habitats (but also appears in the 'conservation' of art objects); 'preservation' usually appears in reference to buildings, objects, and archives (but also wildlife 'preserves'). In the UK, the evolution from 'preservation' to 'conservation' paradigms seems to be part of the tacit knowledge of professionals who manage the natural environment, with 'conservation' representing an enlightened pragmatism, in contrast with the fusty claims of 'preservation' (though their colleagues in curatorial and cultural heritage fields may not recognise this distinction). In the USA the conservation/preservation tension has a subtly different character, associated with twentieth-century negotiations over 'wise use' vs. 'wilderness'. In all of these various contexts, the terms are projected over unpredictable and often unruly objects and environments, in an attempt to 'manage' a way to meaning. In this way, 'conservation' and 'preservation' perform a function not dissimilar to that of the aspic we began with, setting a mould (albeit a quivering, translucent one) around mutable and ephemeral material worlds.

See: Entropy, Palliative curation.

Besanded

St Gothian's Chapel at Gwithian in Cornwall was buried by sand in the thirteenth century. In his *Survey of Cornwall* (1602), Richard Carew reported, "Gwithian, a parish standing near St Ives Baye, muche annoyde with the sea sande, which flyeth at lowe water with the winde out the choked haven into the Lande, swallowing up muche of the lande of the inhabitants, to their great impoverishment". In Breckland, Norfolk, in 1677, John Evelyn, the noted diarist, observed that "The Travelling Sands, about ten miles wide of Euston, that have so damaged the country, rolling from place to place, and like the sands

in the deserts of Libya, quite overwhelmed some gentleman's whole estates". This photograph was taken in Formby, Mersyside, in 2008. It was not a deliberate attempt to bury an expensive new interpretation board but the consequence of rapid coastal change, as the dunes roll landward, besanding boardwalks and interpretation boards alike.

See: Coastal squeeze, Erosion, Managed realignment.

Birds

Would you walk if you could fly? One reason we are drawn to birds is because they have two feet like us and walk about more or less as we do.

But we love them because they fly. This prompts a question about birds that don't. Watching a mute swan or a great bustard (two of the heaviest birds) heaving themselves into flight lifts them into our good books. Penguins seem to fly underwater. But an ostrich? Or a dodo? These are birds that are not quite birds. The dodo was called stupid for its good-natured waddle towards men. They clubbed it to extinction as a reward. Not flying made it unfit. And it was the flight of birds that first secured them a place in our poems and our myths.

Two ravens tumble from the sky cronking and surfing towards the shoulders of Odin, the man-god. One is called Hugin, the other Munin. One whispers into Odin's ears what it has seen; the other, what is to come. They fly with the world's past and its future held in their black eyes. Later, ravens were thought able to predict the outcome of a battle because of their uncanny habit—it seemed—of coming around armies waiting to fight. How did they know? We read them as being able to foretell what was to come; in fact, they read us based on their knowledge of how things had been in the past.

Flight gives birds this supernatural skill. They seem to fly out of the past over our heads and on away from us into the future. Up there, it seems, more time is visible than down here.

See: Extinction, Memory.

Catastrophe

It's the end of the world as we know it, and I feel fine. Anticipating the end of the world, no matter how unpleasant the predicted consequences, is often accompanied by an element of glee that validates its predictor's world-view. Mass extinction, Armageddon, anarchy, ecological apocalypse, and Judgment Day, are all ways of thinking about the end of things that implicitly assert a claim on life's ultimate meaning.

Predicting catastrophe is, among other things, an appropriation of moral legitimacy, whether secular (like the millennium bug, a glitch in computer code, that was going to trigger economic and social collapse), or religious (like US preacher Harold Camping's forecast of the second coming which would 'rapture' two per cent of the world's population to heaven and leave the rest to fend for themselves). In the prediction of catastrophe the soothsayer actually comforts all those who feel uneasy about, say, the rise of the machines, unrestrained industrial capitalism, or the decline in 'traditional' family values.

The prophesized finale contains within it an opportunity for a redemptive validation of a kind that's almost pleasurable, not unlike those cozy catastrophies that repeatedly crop up in post-apocalyptic science-fiction writing typified by John Wyndham, where the male protagonist, let's call him Adam, inexplicably survives the mass extinction of humanity, and is left to repopulate the world with a beautiful young woman who he fortunately meets along the way.

See: Futurology, Uncertainty.

Coastal squeeze

Coastal squeeze is a term used widely in coastal change management.

Coastal squeeze describes beach lowering or habitat loss when the shoreline is constrained from changing position (rolling back) due to an engineered structure such as a coastal defence or by a natural occurrence such as a change in topography, rising ground, or a cliff. An example would be a sand dune, which if unconstrained, would roll landwards as sea levels rise. The same sand dune, if constrained from moving landwards, will react differently. As sea levels rise the sediment (sand) is put into suspension in the water column and transported off-shore, causing the beach level to drop. Recovery of beach levels can be expected as sediment is deposited back on shore through the actions of wave and tide but as sea levels continue to rise the sediment in suspension falls out into increasingly deep water, where tide and wave action fail to reactivate it into the water column and deposit it on the shoreline. The sediment from the eroding sand dune is lost to the system, the beach levels drop and the sand dune erodes.

Coastal squeeze is typically noticed on soft coasts dominated by salt marsh, sand dune and shingle features. It also impacts on hard coasts with the effects being most noticeable in sandy coves where the shoreline is backed by a cliff. Again, as sea levels rise the beach sediment, constrained from moving landward by the natural cliff, disappears and is lost off-shore. The beach levels in our once sandy cove are lowered, exposing boulder and cobble beach material or bedrock. Not so good for sunbathing or building sand castles.

The Marine Climate Change Impacts Partnership (MCCIP) reported in their 2009 score-card that two thirds of shorelines around the UK are showing evidence of beach lowering as a consequence of coastal squeeze and in the majority of cases this lowering was associated with defended frontages. So the very structure that was placed on the shoreline to 'defend' the shoreline is now causing the beach levels to drop. The direct consequence of beach lowering in front of a sea defence is to undermine the foundations of the structure, leading to collapse. The engineering response is to build a bigger sea defence and so the cycle of coastal squeeze begins again—and so on. Each time the cycle turns the costs of the replacement increase dramatically.

We need to learn to live with natural processes, allowing our shorelines room to move and natural sea defences like sand dune and salt marsh the opportunity to move inland in the face of rising sea levels. We need to adapt to rising sea levels by enabling communities and vital infrastructure to be relocated beyond the coastal change risk zone. Expensive in itself and often unpalatable—yet inevitable. Low lying island nations expect to be squeezed out of existence in

Studland, Dorset, where the receding shoreline is forcing the repeated relocation of the beach huts inland, squeezing them between the sea and a SSSI nature reserve.

the not too distant future. The term coastal squeeze invokes a sense of reduction in space for people at the shoreline—we are all being squeezed.

See: Discontinuity, Equilibrium, Erosion.

Collection

"The traditional bunch consists of a collection of watercress stems, about 140mm in length weighing about 110g and held together by a rubber band. The brand name, address and Code of Practice number of the producer should be included on a small rectangular card inserted in the bunch."
'Watercress, production of the cultivated crop', London 1983.

Small-scale watercress cultivation at Alresford, Hampshire. Bunched—around a hundred identification labels.

Around the early 1980s I began to save the card labels that commonly came with bunches of watercress. As well as the grower's name and location, the roughly uniform strips would often state the watery conditions of 'purity', and 'coolness', necessary for commercial production and distribution. Each label—Kingfisher, Lustrecress, Sylvasprings—tethered the cress to a typical and identifiable landscape: a clay and chalk valley with water from a spring or stream, or raised from boreholes, channelled to flow gently across wide beds of screeded concrete and gravel. Seen from above, these planned rectilinear forms impose upon and contrast with the gentle, rolling topography on the ground. But some time in the last ten years such labels have disappeared, along with the rubber band, as the packaging of watercress has changed almost entirely to sealed plastic bags, chilled and loose, and kept fresh at fridge temperature. As with much cultivation, larger sites have been developed and many smaller farms have given up or been absorbed, the number of growers declining in response to the exacting demands of the centralised market. And also during this time it became clear that there was finality to this collection of ephemera, as examples dwindled from occasional to none. No longer is it possible to identify and connect similarity and likeness; the diversity of layouts and colours—these 'printed landscapes'—are now gathered and fixed to the activity and geography of their particular time.

See: Art, Enclosure, Record, Recording.

Commons

Commons is a term used to denote anything that is shared or collectively owned. Traditionally the term has been used to describe the natural environment—the rivers and oceans, the atmosphere, animals and plants, forests and moors—although in Britain at least the term has been used more narrowly to refer to land on which animals could be freely grazed. More recently it has been extended to the cultural sphere: the world wide web, for instance, is often thought of as a virtual commons that everyone shares. There are a number of unwritten laws that pertain to the commons. First, they cannot be commodified. Second, they should be as inclusive as possible. Third, they should be maintained regardless of their return of capital. Fourth, they should be preserved in a state such that they can be handed down to future generations. Fifthly, their value can be added to but must not be degraded.

Despite these injunctions, the commons have been systematically denuded and degraded. This is by no means a recent phenomenon. Since the end of the Holocene (12,000 years before present), humans have been stripping the land of tree cover to facilitate sedentary agriculture. Land has also been appropriated and enclosed by individuals for their own ends for centuries, and culminated in Britain with the Enclosure Acts in the late eighteenth and early nineteenth centuries. Landowners used the Acts to cancel the rights of local people to graze their cattle, cultivate crops, and forage for food, fuel and other materials. Comparable processes took place in colonial contexts, where settlers appropriated land and resources for themselves, and exacted violence on the indigenous populations who relied on the natural environment for their food and shelter.

The industrial revolution really marked the beginning of the end of the global commons. The mills and factories of the nineteenth century consumed large amounts of fossil fuels and in turn polluted the atmosphere, the land and water courses. Industrial-scale farming on land and at sea also led to large-scale pollution events, long-term damage to landscapes and the extinction or denudation of numerous species. We are now in a situation where all the unwritten laws of the commons have been broken. The commons are now almost entirely commodified, such that it is now possible to refer to the natural world as nothing more than a set of 'ecosystem services', in the same manner as, say, an energy provider or a train company. The commons are also now overwhelmingly in the hands of the few; valued only in terms of their monetary value; consumed with no regard for the future; and degraded to such a degree that many environments are little more than wastelands. (Ironically, 'waste' was the term used to describe common land prior to enclosure.) Caring for our global commons is essential for the survival of our species. So why are we so content to commit collective suicide? Writing in the journal *Science* in 1968, Garrett Hardin explained this

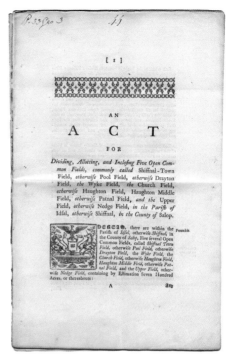

Enclosure Act for Shifnal, Shropshire 1793

most unnatural of impulses. Hardin argued that groups of individuals acting independently and rationally consulting their own self-interest, will deplete a shared resource. While their shared responsibility for the resource was small, their personal gain would be great. The larger the resource, the smaller the shared responsibility, and the greater the exploitation. If you are struggling to conceive of this logic, think about the way we have approached the global fisheries, whether as national or supra-national regulators, producers, or even consumers. Hardin termed this impulse the tragedy of the commons.

See: Catastrophe, Enclosure, Moors.

Continuities

An important part of the current debate concerning climate change revolves around the degree to which it is possible to separate anthropogenic effects from the 'enduring continuities' of natural cycles of change. Defined as such by Daniels and Endfield (2009), in a special issue of *Journal of Historical Geography*, they refer to the pioneering work of Gordon Manley into climate history and the nature of the British climate. This he superbly characterised in *Climate and the British Scene*, written originally in 1952, and related it in a rather deterministic fashion to aspects of the British way of life. He also pointed out the regularities in climate that could be found from any review of the contemporary and historical records. These reinforced cultural experiences provided folklore and traditions, especially in rural communities, which have endured over centuries. Manley voiced a wider feeling that environments and landscapes, in the broadest sense of the words, exhibited regularities that were somehow intrinsic and needed to be identified and cherished.

Identifying and defining such continuities poses a number of problems. Continuities will vary with the perspective of the observer. On the moors of West Penwith continuity is seen as retaining the status quo, a landscape which, in its current form, owes much to relatively recent management practices, and has little that could be said to be enduring in nature, either in terms of its origins or future. Elements of the moors, the tors, gorse and heaths can claim some antiquity but their arrangement and appearance relative to one another do not. Identifying the key character of what is enduring is therefore difficult and often an artificial construct, or as Cronon argues in *The Journal of American History* in 1992, "we force our stories on a world that doesn't fit them".

See: Discontinuity, Longue durée, Moors, Presentism.

Cycle of erosion

William Morris Davis (1850–1935) explained river valley morphology through a cycle of erosion, 'The Geographical Cycle', from mountain stream to middle valley to broad peneplain, the river growing from youth through middle to old age.

In the early world a boy lived on a hill. For seven years he walked the garden finding bugs and flowers, never wondering about over-the-wall. The gate stayed shut, the old creaky hinge never having the chance to creak and warn the boy of visitors. Early one May morning, asleep in the outhouse, the boy stirred to a click, a creak, a gentle tap and thud, a creak and a click again. Peering to see what the sound might have brought, eyes lit on a bicycle, bright in the dawn before breakfast.

After eggs and bread, the boy examined the machine, a gift to explore. Balance achieved from a few turns of the lawn, the boy considered the garden gate. What had come in should go out. A click, a creak, a creak, a click, and the boy was through the wall.

With perfect sight he saw downhill all round, the world's bare slope, distance as far as a haze of far moisture. The hilltop boy had heard of sea, but never heard sea. The moisture must be sea, and quickly to the saddle, the boy lifted feet to pedals, though with the world downhill the pedals were only footrests for the duration.

The steep hill hurtled the bicycle on, wheels cutting dusty ground, the boy looking to scenes one side and another. Balance tilting slightly, the straight course shifted, but flight soon adjusted, direction regained. For days of delight the ride went, until the boy noticed that, unlike the bicycles he had seen in catalogues, this model lacked brakes. There was no stopping.

Without food since the breakfast eggs and bread, days of delight ago, the boy rocked tired in the saddle. The bicycle swept to curve downslope, ever wider, wheels grooving dust. Along the machine swept, the boy past taking in scenery, fainting hungry, bicycle veering, curving out, dust incised, balance tipping. The boy arrived at sleep, or something like sleep. Reaching the haze seen from the hilltop days before, the bicycle tippled the boy to a wide beach, sea waves touching tyres as it fell in a final sweep of wheel, the boy washed by the sea he neither heard nor saw.

Three days later, clouds came to the hilltop, the first since records began, their rain making tyre tracks a river, flowing in lines and meanders to the sea, where they bore a body out (and in again) with the tide.

See: Entropy, Epiphany, Erosion.

Discontinuity

In its strict geological meaning a discontinuity is a surface at which seismic waves change their velocity, usually a fault or a bedding plane, the most famous being the Mohorovičić Discontinuity between the crust and the mantle. This provides a useful analogue for broader applications, both in space and time. Any sharp division can be seen as a discontinuity, with associated ideas of abrupt change. There is for instance a textural discontinuity hypothesis that links animal body mass to landscape texture available for exploitation. This seeks to explain the possible impact of landscape structures on animals and adds a further dimension to the management of ecosystems. We already know of the importance of corridors between biogeographic islands; this hypothesis shows that the nature of the organisms themselves can be affected by the existence of certain types of structure within a landscape, especially the existence of discontinuities. It has also been argued by landscape geneticists that the structures themselves can hide continuities at the genetic level, properties of importance for ecosystems—undermining the idea of cheerful islands of community patches sitting in a hostile matrix made up of different species, and likely separated by abrupt boundaries.

In natural landscapes discontinuities are not always sharp and well defined; there may be ecotones or areas of transition from one community to another. Natural treelines are rarely abrupt when seen from the ground although they may appear highly discontinuous from a distance—it tends to be a matter of scale. The discontinuity between land and sea, land and water, varies with a regular temporal pattern and over long timescales, hundreds of years at least sea level itself changes. The traces of these changes are there to be read in a landscape of abandoned cliffs or drowned valleys, or even in the historical record. In the Baltic where the land is still rising in response to the loss of ice 10,000 years ago the abrupt land/sea margin is a matter of historical record. In human terms abrupt breaks can be arbitrary, lines on maps that bear little relation to what is happening on the ground, and it is our need to organise and divide that produces apparently abrupt changes.

Discontinuities can imply discomfort, either due to the arbitrary nature of the change or to the alteration of a known feature, although as J. B. Jackson, the American writer and artist noted: "there has to be that interval of neglect, there has to be discontinuity... the necessity for ruins (which) provide the incentive for restoration, and a return to origins." It is interesting that attention is being turned to abandoned brownfield sites as havens of biodiversity, places which are very much set apart yet providing new foci for natural plant and animal communities.

See: Continuities, Erosion, Uncertainty, Zone of exclusion.

Dream-map

If mapping is often associated with delimiting, bounding, and fixing the landscape, then the dream-map represents its shadow side. Cartography is frequently employed as a means of visualising past and future landscapes. But a positivistic approach confines maps to recording what is observable in the landscape. The dream-map can reveal the unmanifest qualities of a place discovered by other means. It permits the visualisation of (im)possibility and imagination.

The incorporation of dreams seems antithetical to the project of cartography. After all, if dreams represent the irrational, how can they be appropriate for a task that depends on accuracy? This contradiction is not at all self-evident if we turn to examples from non-Western cultures. At a public hearing in British Columbia on a proposed oil pipeline, Hugh Brody was shown a First Nations dream-map. The map was only unwrapped at times of special importance: a piece of moosehide as large as a tabletop, covered with colourful markings. These charted the trails across the area: "Up here is heaven; this is the trail that must be followed; here is a wrong direction; this is where it would be worst of all to go; and over there are all the animals. They explained that all of this had been discovered in dreams."

This dream-map described in Brody's *Maps and Dreams*, reflects the cosmology of the culture that created it—it would be inappropriate and disingenuous to imitate it. But it is a salutary reminder of the important role of chance and intuition in constructing environmental knowledge, even in discoveries elicited by scientific fieldwork. A recent spate of books on 'wildness' are often hinged around these oneiric encounters with nature—Jay Griffiths' book *Wild* in particular emphasises the importance of dreams within indigenous cultures. If nothing else, the popularity of these books prompts us to reflect on those emotional—sometimes epiphanic—experiences that can constitute our most profound encounters with the natural world.

See: Art, Epiphany, Place.

Ebb and flood

A group gathered to consider 'Anticipatory Histories' in the presence of the Tamar. A meeting to ponder questions of historic flood and nature power, at the National Trust's Cotehele property, on the Tamar's steep Cornwall slope, was accompanied by the tidal river rising to unusual height. Cotehele shows gardens, historic building, tea room, and historic craft museumed and moored on the property quayside. Attention moved from all attractions to the river. Would Tamar touch tea room? Might a flood meeting relocate under water rise?

River Tamar, Cotehele, Cornwall

A most significant site at Cotehele is a straight horizontal line, the base of tree branch spread, a line under which attempted growth would be under regular water. Sea shapes riverbank wood. Hilly Cotehele comes down to horizontals. Sedimented river (down, up and so on), below mud shown and covered, below trees (full as ever above the line) cut off from branching. A high rail viaduct a mile downstream, arboreal trim on the Devon bank, Tamar's valley levels.

See: Adaptation, Tides.

Enclosure

How should we feel about field boundaries? They divide opinion just as they demarcate different land uses. The answer depends on how we look at them, not to mention when and where we happen to be standing. Seen from a distance and an elevated position, a landscape cross-cut by hedges evokes orderliness and even a certain homeliness. It is no coincidence that we often refer to such landscapes as patchwork quilts. Many nations celebrate these landscapes as the embodiment of their identity. In Britain, for instance, small, oddly shaped fields in green or rusty hues symbolise a nation that thinks of itself as old and eccentric, while

Extract from West Penwith Survey at Rosemergy. The northern and central parts of the survey map lynchets and earthworks within modern fields, whose patterns derive from the late prehistoric period.

in the USA huge oblongs of wheat act as reminders of a pioneering spirit. These attitudes obscure a contested history of enclosure. In Britain the enclosure of open fields and common land was a part of the revolution in agricultural practices that gained pace in the eighteenth century. When Parliamentary Acts were used to force through the enclosure of land, it was usually to the good of a few large landowners and to the detriment of the poor. The enclosure of land in other contexts—whether the plains of the American Midwest or the forests of India—similarly resulted in the dispossession of indigenous peoples from their sources of food, shelter and livelihood. More recently, field boundaries were derided as oppositions to progress and were systematically removed to allow farmers to use larger machinery and improve productivity. The result was a severe reduction in species diversity as an important habitat was removed. Today hedges, walls and fences tend to be celebrated and cherished. They are often several thousands of years old and literally trace the margins of ancient settlements. They cut down on soil erosion by protecting land from wind. They are recognised to be havens for many species of animals and plants, such as the cirl bunting, the robin and wren, seven species of bats, small mammals like voles and shrews, as well as reptiles and amphibians. So where should we stand on enclosure? Is it good or bad? Is it even helpful to ask that question? Instead, perhaps we might think of enclosure as an example of a human modification of land that slips from its moorings, and accept that each generation makes the enclosure it needs.

See: Commons, Discontinuity, Moors.

Entropy

The tendency to disorder or chaos encapsulated in the Second Law of Thermodynamics is a theme that crosses easily from its scientific home, where it is viewed as an intrinsic property of irreversible systems, to the arts and humanities in general, as encapsulated by Byron:

> I had a dream, which was not all a dream.
> The bright sun was extinguish'd, and the stars
> Did wander darkling in the eternal space,
> Rayless, and pathless, and the icy earth
> Swung blind and blackening in the moonless air;
> Morn came, and went—and came, and brought no day.

Indeed poets and playwrights have been remarkably successful in communicating the idea of entropy to wider audiences. It is one of the underlying themes of Stoppard's 'Arcadia' where characters seek to discover order and regularity among seeming chaos. As Septimus mixes the jam into his rice pudding, he is asked to consider whether it is not odd that if he stirs backwards the jam does not reconstitute itself.

Because we see order in most things we do and there is something of an innate human desire to impart order to a potentially chaotic world, few societies would be happy to see a loss of control over their environment, which would then fall into disorder as the result of 'natural' processes. A healthy level of entropy thus goes against a general desire humans have to suck orderliness from their natural environment, to paraphrase the physicist Schrödinger. It is an interesting question as to whether when people view landscapes it is the order or the disorder that they see and value; judging the Goldilocks level of entropy that satisfactorily aligns landscape 'health' with human feelings of wellbeing is something of an impossible goal. Ecologists in particular have looked at ways of measuring entropy in the landscape. As plant communities become more and more fragmented due to the encroachment of the built environment this can be measured in terms of disorder or entropy. Ironically, however, this can also result in increased diversity, especially in terms of habitats. Thus, as entropy increases so does diversity.

Do not see: Equilibrium. *See:* Aspic, Discontinuity.

Epiphany

Epiphany has its roots in religion—it is a Christian festival. More generally 'epiphany' refers to a moment of sudden or great revelation —which is the way I use it here. Epiphanies are often what set us off on a particular course in life. In my own case, I had a succession of reinforcing epiphanies that made me into a naturalist and a scientist.

The earliest I can remember occurred when I was about four years old when I climbed to the nest of a song thrush in the garden and held one of its sky-blue eggs in my hand (I broke it!). Another occurred when I was eleven and was taken to Bardsey Island, off the tip of the Llyn Peninsula in North Wales, one glorious summer day to see the choughs, and seals. As we walked back across the island to the boat at the end of the day we saw a young man with a notebook sitting beside a telescope: my father said to me "You could do something like that when you are older". And I did: that visit to Bardsey set the course for my entire life—studying birds on beautiful islands.

An epiphany is an emotional response, directing us on a course of action. An epiphany can turn someone into a natural historian, and in some cases into a professional biologist. Scientists are often assumed to be devoid of emotion, studying the natural world with detached objectivity, but this is mistaken. Most biologists that I know had epiphanies, and most continue to have a deep emotional involvement with the natural world—with landscape and with nature. It is what motivates them to discover how the natural world works.

See: Birds, Natural history.

Equilibrium

Equilibrium is a much favoured concept in ecology and geomorphology and appears in a range of applications, most of which use graphical form to show how systems operate over time. Outside its scientific meaning, the idea of equilibrium is usually associated with 'balance', indicating no overall change in what is being described so long as this balance is retained. In reality there are few, if any, occasions that achieve true balance and an effective preservation of forms. Thus, for any landscape, equilibrium must be understood within a general background context of change. Along coasts, for instance, no matter how much effort is put into looking for an equilibrium state that retains the form of a beach or cliffline, there will be some underlying trend changing the physical landscape and remodelling the cliff (so long as sea level remains relatively constant). Usually this situation is described as a 'dynamic equilibrium', which acknowledges the underlying trend—a concept that can be difficult to grasp when change is relatively slow and beyond human timescales for perception. Following major 'events' such as floods, or even extreme events such as hurricanes, the idea of a return to equilibrium in some newly altered state is perhaps easier to comprehend and accept. Where there is intervention to 'preserve' or 'protect' then the pursuit of equilibrium is sometimes expressed in a desire to budget, which conceives of change as a loss requiring a balancing input. Demands for coastal protection can therefore be simply understood as a profit and loss accounting, with loss of beach requiring artificial compensation—a matter of balancing the budget.

The search for equilibrium can be seen at all scales, from a Gaian desire for planetary health to the

Pwll Du Bay on the Gower peninsula, where a shingle ridge is very gradually moving inland towards two dwellings.

extremely local. There is perhaps little doubt that at the planetary scale equilibrium is a necessary and valuable property—a 'good thing'—but without recognition of the range of equilibria that occur at smaller scales there is a danger that defence of equilibrium for its own sake can lead to wider, unforeseen consequences. With climate change, the lack of consistency in one of the main driving forces behind natural systems (namely, climate and weather systems) complicates our understanding of how plant communities or broader landscapes will develop. Defining the health of such systems, which has long been linked to the identification and attempted maintenance of some state of equilibrium that will allow for survival, will become more difficult.

Do not see: Entropy. *See:* Shifting baseline syndrome.

Erosion

Erosion occurs at the coast as a consequence of wave energy reaching the shoreline. Soft coasts such as salt marsh, sand dune and certain cliffs are particularly vulnerable. Soft coastlines retreat at different rates according to their geology. At Birling Gap in East Sussex the chalk cliffs are retreating at a rate of 1m per year, although events tend to be episodic, with a section of cliff suffering structural failure on a localised front. The retreat can be as much as ten metres in a single event.

Coastal erosion increases as wave energy reaching the shore increases. Future climate change scenarios suggest that the frequency of storms may not increase but their intensity might, meaning an increase in wave energy reaching the shoreline and a consequent increase in coastal erosion. But it's not all bad. Eroded material forms sediment in the inshore marine area and this useful additional material can, through long-shore drift, be of benefit to shorelines down-drift, enabling accretion to take place. Groynes are often used as a sea defence measure to slow sediment transport away from one part of the coast. This deprives those areas down drift of a new source of sediment.

Erosion and retreating shorelines reveal features from the historic environment. There is a greater emphasis now being placed on recording these features and understanding the stories these glimpses of the past can tell before they are lost to the sea. Archaeologists are increasingly comfortable with this approach. Erosion may cause the loss of significant features in the historic environment but it can also reveal new significance like the Formby footprints, shown here, revealed by the eroding sand dunes and enabling us to see human footprints captured in soft sediments some 4,500 years ago before the dunes were deposited on top.

Erosion can of course refer to loss of non-physical features. We talk often of values being eroded, but as with physical erosion, is it always loss? Or do we really mean change? A change of attitude, a change in our view of the world or in the case of erosion at the shoreline, a change as sediment moves from one part of the coast to another.

See: Art, Coastal squeeze, Cycle of erosion.

Footprint trail, Formby

Extinction

X; ex-; s̶t̶r̶u̶c̶k̶ ̶t̶h̶r̶o̶u̶g̶h̶; killed off; wiped out; done for; all over.

Extinction is best understood as an anthropocentric condition snared in a matrix of evolution, culture, economics, conservation and politics. In the modern era, species disappearance was a fate defined by two icons, the dodo and the dinosaur. The coining of the popular phrase—'dead as a dodo'—was borne of the realisation that we humans can witness the passing of the last of a kind. Often enough it was a status meted out *by* us, as a colonising and destructive presence that over-hunted, polluted or cleared naturally occurring habitats. Fossil discoveries confirmed that the categorical death of a species-type could be backdated too. Enlightened, with a pre-historical consciousness, we learned to use mass extinction events, like those of the dinosaurs, to help define formal time boundaries; of geological, environmental and biological events, taking place in a former Earth. And in the process, we discovered that earlier cases of species disappearance were not always

down to us. Consider briefly, *Megaloceros giganteus*, the Irish Elk (right). Its decline and ultimate demise was the result of post-glacial climate changes altering the available vegetation mix and shortening the critical feeding season; processes that long preceded the arrival of early man in Ireland.

In the popular imagination, these were the true times when—whether for good or for ill—'all gone' really did mean *all gone*. Gone as an indisputable condition, and extinction as something absolute. And now? Perhaps it is the mounting burden of loss and the lengthening list of the missing from floral and faunal kingdoms, that give not only cause for regret, but act as prompt for creative kinds of response. Today the sciences and the arts toy with the promise of rebirth and return, offering reprieve to the long since dead.

Developmental biologists claim that samples of soft tissue from woolly mammoth corpses—kept safe in cold storage by Siberian perma-frost for thousands of years—will enable DNA to be extracted and then inserted into African elephant eggs. Controversial trials in genetic cloning are said to be underway. The more credible the claims of immanent success, the looser seems the scientific logic. Sensationalised by Michael Crichton and Steven Spielberg, first as bestseller then box-office hit, the vitalist stuff of cryogenics has always seemed cranky and cack-handed, heavily dependent on a slack-jawed and bug-eyed brand of spectatorship, of the sort dramatised to perfection by Jeff Goldblum.

Sanity and sobriety prevail in contemporary art, where episodes from the annals of natural history are used, for pragmatic end and imaginative purpose, to inform and instruct on ways to care for the future. Case studies of environmental art proliferate. Kate Foster's are exemplary (http://www.meansealevel.net/; http://www.blueantelope.info/). Asking how a culture remembers the species it has eradicated, hers is the pin that pricks at consciences in the present, and the parable concentrating attentions on the plight of still living but vulnerable populations. In this fashion, cultural afterlives are attached to biological futures, myths of long-standing twinned with miraculous kinds of outcome.

See: Art.

Futurology

As if the world didn't have enough '-ologies', then up pops another. Often misunderstood (or misapplied), futurology is translated by the popular media as the profession of charlatans, of modern-day soothsayers trying to predict the next big thing. It's a world of flying cars and robot servants. Of miracle cures and technofixes. Yet this cautious attitude towards future predicting has a deserved pedigree. From the Delphic Oracle to the Witch of Endor, from Nostradamus to Mystic Meg, and from the South Sea Bubble to the recent Crash, mysticism and claims of supra-human predictive knowledge have often attracted fools, with their money, their pride—or their lives—being easily parted.

And yet, perhaps the human soul is too cynical about the future. How quick we are to say "the future can look after itself", and face the future with wilful futility. We wait to "cross that bridge when we get to it". And in the words of the popular song, we are advised "Que sera sera, Whatever will be will be, The future's not ours to see, Que sera sera".

We perhaps take this stance because we know there's true wisdom in the motto from an early colonial American almanac which reminds us that "unto this do predictions belong, either they are right, or they are wrong". Or in the words of Donald Rumsfeld: "[T]here are known knowns; there are things we know we know. We also know there are known unknowns; that is to say we know there are some things we do not know. But there are also unknown unknowns—the ones we don't know we don't know."

Futurology is perhaps at its worst when it seeks to predict. It is at its best where it seeks to explore. Futurology isn't about the long-range weather forecast. It's more like archaeology, excavating the future, dusting off different signals and imagining possibilities which explain what we're finding.

See: Catastophe, Uncertainty.

Introductions

Has a pheasant ever been known to do anything interesting? Why do we despise introduced animals? Certainly some have tipped the balance and wrought havoc with native populations. Weeds and invasives, aliens and asylum seekers, the language of involuntary migrants is heavy with hate.

But in what way are they to blame? Study the ruddy duck. This North American stiff-tailed duck was released on to British waters by bird-lovers. It thrived and brightened dour days of reservoir bird-watching. But it also had nefarious ambitions or was imagined to have them. Birds from Britain found their way to Spain where another native stiff-tail, the white-headed duck, was struggling to survive already. The ruddy made advances on the white-headed but the genetic swamping of a native by an alien couldn't be allowed to proceed. Cue gunmen across southern Britain crouching in reedbeds and attempting to shoot all ruddy ducks and thereby tidy up nature.

Animal introductions are apt expressions of our botched tenancy of the planet. 'Plastics' we used to call them when I was keen to boost my list of birds seen and wondered what exactly was admissible as 'wild'. A Chilean flamingo on the grey mudflats of Bridgwater Bay in Somerset looked like an abandoned wedding dress and couldn't be ticked. But little owls? They are only here because they were released. And the red kites that swoop over back gardens in Didcot. And the capercaillie is only now a British bird because introduced birds replaced the extinct population. Think of the European starling in North America. A nineteenth century drug manufacturer, sensing some deficit in the native avifauna, planned to introduce all the birds mentioned in Shakespeare. He would have shipped in a phoenix if he could. Starlings were released in Central Park in New York City and did what other Europeans had done: survived, prospered, and moved west. Now they are in Alaska and are among the commonest birds on the continent. They are widely hated.

The pheasant population—British since the Romans perhaps—is topped up every year by millions of released birds. Birders think of them as trash and even hunters cannot sell their meat. The corpses are regularly ploughed back into the soil to assist in the rearing of next year's birds.

See: Acclimatisation, Rewilding.

Liminal zone

Deriving from the latin word *limin* for threshold, the term liminal was coined as a concept in twentieth-century anthropology, to describe a state of transitional 'in-betweeness', notably in rites of passage. Liminal has expanded as an interpretative keyword, to encompass various forms of cultural and psychological study, beyond designating a social process, or a human condition, to focusing on the various places where liminality is presumed to be active, perhaps with a degree of environmental agency. Hence the current interest in 'liminal zones', the thresholds between apparently well established sites and spaces: land and sea, country and city, earth and sky, day and night, interior and exterior, reality and virtuality, spirit and matter, order and disorder, sacred and profane. So liminal zones include shorelines, cliff tops, suburbs, bridges, airports, windows, doorways, fairgrounds, websites, twilights, graveyards and haunted houses, but also more fluent, conspicuously socially constructed spaces like those of pilgrimage and carnival, puberty and senility, which conserve the original anthropological connotation. The expressly geographical framing of liminality has converged with a tendency from depth psychology, the desire for a creative space of permanent liminality, and a more widespread trope of avant-garde art and culture. They seek to explore and occupy places at the margin, peripheries at or beyond the boundaries of established social spaces, to observe in new exposures cutting edge, excessive processes of cultural and physical development and destruction (including documenting disappearing forms of landscape and livelihood) and cultivate an edgy, outsider status. Hence the early twentieth-century migration of bohemian artists to colonize coastal parts of Cornwall and later in the century to the class frontier of Hackney, often leaving in their wake a wider and longer process of gentrification. Shoreline aesthetics in current artwork arguably owe something to the celebrated example of Derek Jarman's garden at Dungeness, as to expressly ecological aesthetics concerning sea levels. The current fashion for walking as a condition of creative writing, has expanded the repertoire of liminal zones, with some canonical sites of ruination such as W. G. Sebald's crumbling Suffolk cliffs and Iain Sinclair's derelict inner London waterways. Such edgelands, as they have now been dubbed, are seemingly unsociable on the ground, but increasingly overcrowded on the page, colonized by deep topographers, new nature writers, literary cartographers and psychogeographers, in works which sometimes unwittingly re-enact traditions of landscape connoisseurship. With their picturesque mix of technological detritus and flourishing wildlife, such edgelands seem increasingly conventional, more central than peripheral to the cultural imagination, liminal zones passing into landscape scenery.

See: Discontinuity, Nature writing, Rewilding.

Living landscapes

The bigger picture: a living landscape is a wildlife-rich, ecologically functioning landscape that can adapt to pressures such as climate change. Living landscapes engage and embrace communities and give people a place to live, work and play. On a physical level living landscapes can be defined as (opposite):

See: Adaptation, Commons.

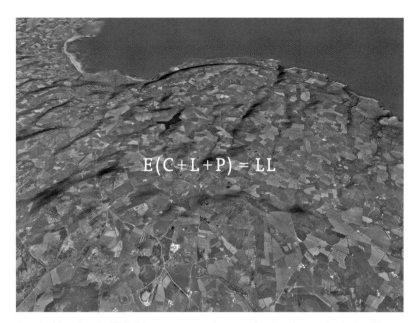

$$E(C+L+P) = LL$$

C = a healthy suite of wildlife rich *core* areas such as nature reserves and wildlife sites from which wildlife can spread out into the wider landscape; L = a vibrant network of rivers and streams, hedges, waysides and stepping stones of new or restored habitat that *link* wildlife areas from coast to coast and from moor to town and village; P = a working wider countryside that is managed so that plants and animals will be able to move through this *permeable* landscape, enabling them to adapt to climate change; E = involvement and *engagement* of local communities in the establishment, maintenance and enjoyment of a living landscape.

Satellite picture: Penwith moors to the south coast of Cornwall.

Longue durée

Fernand Braudel, a pioneer of the *Annales* school of history, sought to show how history moved to a longer, deeper, beat. I was taught about this concept by a man dressed as a security guard; our lecturer was moonlighting to make ends meet and had just come off the night-shift. He later stood as a BNP candidate, but that's another story, and should not overshadow the brilliance of Braudel.

What Braudel recognized was that as much as we focus on events and individuals, it is the long rhythms of life which make our history. Like an Ant not seeing the Elephant, human lives are so short so as to not see the whole story. Lives are brief episodes shaped by the grand narrative.

Yet, this idea of the long game can produce both useful and useless thoughts, when thinking about conservation and change. On the useful side it can help one understand inevitabilities shaped by the long and deep trends. On the useless side it can reduce responses to change to futilism: a feeling that everything is so big there is little that one can do.

Victor Frankl, a pioneer of a useful but (for many) lesser known school of psychoanalysis (born out of his experiences of Auschwitz), offers some solace here. His advice guides us to refocus our emotions into more positive places. Whilst there may be big forces shaping things in ways which seem to be beyond our control, Frankl's approach is to remind us that even when we are without choice, we have ultimate freedom in deciding how we want to respond to that lack of choice. We can choose humour, joy, angst, futilism, contradiction, denial, anger, celebration, opposition, remembrance, avoidance, embracing—in fact an endless list of responses. So, when the metaphorical and literal tide turns against us, it is perhaps important to recognise and accept the inevitability of some of the long forces at play, but at the same time also be liberated, by consciously recognising the range of emotional and practical responses that are open to us as places change.

See: Continuities, Futurology, Temprocentrism.

Managed realignment

How has the world changed since optical magnification became widely available? Looking down a telescope effects a realignment of perception. If you read Ted Hughes' bird poems you can tell he used binoculars. His thrushes are terrifying partly because he has been able to watch them close up. The earth-moving that managed realignment suggests has a similar effect. It will alter how things seem as well as how they are, how they live in the mind as well as how they are felt underfoot.

Inland from the tidal edge of the Wash are a series of banks. These are old seawalls and dykes built into the sea to allow for intakes of marshland. We can read the advance of dry over wet. Hundreds of yards every century. Elsewhere in East Anglia the banks have been deliberately broken and sea-water flows in. Wet over dry. The porous edge is back. Having been, as a people, graduates of the King Canute school of land management we have matured into wiser mudlarks. The dynamism of silt and the energy of water are great and humbling teachers. The terminology might stink—letting go, the nonce term for sacking, is a near neighbour—but the possibilities of life without barricades is revolutionary.

See: Coastal squeeze, Ebb and flood, Tides.

Memory

In everyday thinking we tend to think of memory as something we possess, something fixed and stable and stored away in our mental filing cabinet to be subsequently retrieved relatively intact. In his essay on human understanding, seventeenth century philosopher John Locke writes of memory in this way, as a repository, a way of retention: "This is memory, which is as it were the storehouse of our ideas". The storage model metaphor is attractive because it fits with our ideas about the sovereign subject and the persistence of the self.

But it also lends itself to a problematic commonsense temporality—a fairly recent way of thinking about time that arose at the turn of the seventeenth and eighteenth century—where time, first, is conceived as a succession of instants proceeding in a flat horizontal line (reflected in the way memory seems to retrieve or revive a previous event) and second, where time is separated out from space *a priori* (reflected in the way 'the past' becomes a place spatially distinguished from the present allowing us to visit it). This commonsense temporality gets carried forward in all sorts of state practices from law, medicine, geopolitics, town planning and academia, through to its application par excellence in the heritage and museum sector where notions of conservation, inheritance, provenance, truth, and authenticity, leave resource managers with the Sisyphean task of denying that they are producing something new.

See: Aspic, Presentism, Temprocentrism.

Monitoring

In 2010 a team of researchers from the Universities of Oxford and Cambridge reported on a new monitoring technology they were using to study badgers' behaviour underground. Special collars had been attached to the animals and were picked up by an antenna on the forest floor above their setts. The antenna emitted low frequency magnetic fields of different strengths that could locate the animals underground. About 250,000 items of data were collected on the chip attached to the badgers' collars and downloaded onto a local base station whenever a badger emerged above ground. Over a one month period a staggering seven million readings were collected on the movement of just four badgers, the aim being to learn more about badgers' social lives underground. This extraordinary level of scrutiny was actually nothing new to these badgers. They had been monitored in one way or another since 1987, largely because they had chosen to take up residence in Wytham Wood, which is owned by the University of Oxford and used by their Wildlife Conservation Research Unit. It is one of the most heavily monitored temperate woodlands in the world.

The sensor networks used to monitor the Wytham badgers are being employed in a range of other environmental contexts. These include oceanic and volcanic monitoring, the study of cattle, and the movement of glaciers. Those developing the technology have promised the collection of spatio-temporal data at "unprecedented granularities", not to mention a revolution in how scientists perform field experiments. Certainly it seems a long way from the use of quadrats and tape measures, the stock-in-trade of environmental surveyors. The effect of course is the same—the ability to trace changes and patterns in the natural world over time and across space, whether in terms of fluctuating populations of species or the changing composition of habitats, the slow slide of a glacier or the foraging activities of a badger. Monitoring, however technologically advanced, is fundamental to successful nature conservation. It highlights the problems and crises experienced by animals, plants, water, land and air; helps set conservation priorities; and tells us of the success or otherwise of particular management practices. But there are nonetheless a few nagging doubts. Like unwitting participants in a reality TV show, the Wytham badgers no longer have private lives. Do we now know too much about the previously secret lives of animals? And what are the cultural effects of such unprecedented granularities of knowing? Perhaps the more we know about nature the less we can imagine?

See: Acclimatisation, Record; Recording.

Moor

In Britain moors act as the nation's wilderness. To reinforce this role many of them have been protected as National Parks. The Peak District, the Brecon Beacons, the North York Moors, the Cairngorms, Dartmoor and Exmoor—all share similar natural characteristics as moorland. Britain's moors are usually well above sea level, mostly hilly and occasionally mountainous. Their soil quality is usually acidic and rainfall is high. As a result they are dominated by low growing vegetation, such as heather and bracken, and feature few trees. Their ability to support agricultural activities is often limited to grazing for sheep and their human populations are sparse and scattered. However, evidence of human settlement upon Britain's moorlands extends back thousands of years. Barrows, tolmens and other archaeological features abound, as do ancient walls and hedges. Their apparent desolation and inhospitability made them a popular site for the Romantics in the early nineteenth century and they regularly featured as an important backdrop for many gothic novels. *The Hound of the Baskervilles* saw Sherlock Holmes combat the dreadful creature across the treacherous bogs of Dartmoor; Emily Brontë's *Wuthering Heights* was set on Yorkshire's moorland.

Paradoxically, as the romantics portrayed Britain's moors as sites of tragedy and horror, they also popularised them as sites of tourism and leisure. By the mid-nineteenth century tourists were heading to the moors in increasing numbers. They were places of escape from the trappings of civilisation, and more prosaically, from the druggery of work. The arrival of increasing numbers of tourists to the moors in the twentieth century, especially from Britain's big conurbations, resulted in conflict between the landowners and those demanding the right to roam across these seemingly wide, open spaces. It culminated with the so-called Kinder Scout mass trespass on 24 April 1932, when a number of hikers deliberately trespassed onto private land in the Peak District in protest at the private ownership of Britain's natural landscapes. These disputes resolved in the favour of the hikers and holiday-makers, although conflicts over the management of Britain's moorlands continue. In west Cornwall for instance, the National Trust, in partnership with other organisations, recently introduced a set of traditional farming practices—grazing, scrub clearance, bracken control and burning—across West Penwith, with the aim of restoring the rare lowland heath landscape (see pp.13–15). The erection of fences, the clearing of land and building of cattle grids was greeted with indignation by local groups, who worried that fences would restrict access and possibly lead back to the situation against which the Kinder Scout hikers were protesting. Fences, they claimed, would also ruin an ancient and wild landscape.

Seen from a distance moors are elemental and under-determined. We might speculate that it is this quality of moors that we find so enticing: it is easy to project our own desires onto these blank canvasses. If so, perhaps that is why they so frequently become the site of conflict over what and who the environment is for.

See: Commons, Enclosure.

Museum

As a young boy, the highlight of a visit to Cornwall's county museum was the Egyptian mummy. Although I had only a vague idea where it had come from I certainly appreciated its exoticism, not to mention of course its more gothic associations. It didn't occur to me to question why there was an Egyptian mummy in a museum in west Cornwall in the first place. After all, museums were all about the display of outlandish, exceptional objects, weren't they? (I'd also been to the Natural History Museum in London and seen their dinosaur skeletons so I was something of an expert on the matter.) In fact, the subject of what museums should represent and whom they should cater for was quite a contentious one and had been so since at least the nineteenth century.

The early modern equivalents to today's museums were known as cabinets of curiosities, which were collections of miscellaneous exotic objects—including perhaps minerals, shells, stuffed animals and human artifacts—amassed by wealthy private collectors and accessible only to their family and friends. They were often displayed in purpose-

The 'space-for-time' geology display, Haslemere Educational Museum, Haslemere, Surrey.

built cabinets (hence the name), or sometimes in dedicated rooms. An increasing belief in the importance of access to knowledge and education—and specifically in the *improving* nature of didacticism— provided a new role for museums in the nineteenth century. As more museums opened their doors to the wider paying public, rather than just to subscribers or men of science, they had to reconsider their purpose and practices. Who exactly was the museum's public—did it include women, children, and working men, for instance? How much information should be provided to visitors regarding the objects in front of them? And what should museums display? Visitors answered the last question with their feet: the more exotic the better. However, while the Egyptian mummies and dinosaur bones pulled in the crowds, others urged museums to play their part in the study and appreciation of the local region. As a result the store rooms of regional museums today are full of local collections that were donated or bought for them, sometimes several hundred years ago. Wander the stacks and you will come across stuffed birds in cases, drawers of shells and preserved insects, models of archaeological remains and antiquarian objects, all with a local provenance. Many of these collections no longer find themselves on display anymore, but they remain invaluable to those interested in tracing the changes that have occurred in place over time. Want to know if a recently discovered plant species is the first of its kind in a particular place? It's likely that your local museum holds a dried herbarium, or *hortus siccus*, of the region's plants that will help you determine an answer. Museums today have a vital role to play in telling us what our locality was like in the past, but in doing so they can also help us to envision what it might be like in the future.

See: Collection, Record, Recording.

Natural history

This is the study of the natural world. It can take many forms and has changed over time. In the Middle Ages animals and plants were valued for their religious and medicinal properties, epitomised by the so called 'doctrine of signatures'. A condition like scarlet fever for example could be cured by possessing or eating a red bird such as a crossbill or bullfinch. Similarly, a pulmonary condition could be cured by lungwort—whose leaves resembled the human lung. The doctrine of signatures is based on the notion that the similarity in appearance between the animal and plant and the condition was God's way of pointing out a cure. God didn't always make this easy, sometimes his clues had to be de-coded, sometimes they were apparent only to a chosen few. The basic message was to look to nature for moral guidance and God's help.

The image of the pelican piercing its breast in order to feed its offspring on its own blood was widely reproduced in Medieval times. The pelican was a symbol of a selfless Christ, and the image appears in misericords, lecterns and other bits of church furniture. Those who created such images were rarely ornithologists and it is sometimes difficult to identify the bird as a pelican. A pelican on a misericord in Lavenham church in Suffolk, looks more like a thrush. The origin of the pelican-as-Christ image probably arose as a result of someone witnessing a flamingo feeding its offspring. Flamingos feed their young on brine shrimp which are red and they deliver it as a red soup dribbled into the chick's mouth. It is easy to imagine how such a straightforward bit of natural history might be elaborated in the telling into something with religious connotations.

It was the obsession with moral instruction that resulted in the first natural history encyclopaedias, which were published in the 1500s and early 1600s by Conrad Gessner and Ullyses Aldrovandi. These present a mish-mash of turgid information: everything you thought you ever needed to know about a particular species in terms of its mythology,

'Eagle' and chicks
The image of a bird piercing its breast to revive its chicks by allowing them to feed on the parent's blood is a powerful and widespread emblem dating back to the Middle Ages. In this image of self-sacrifice the parent bird represents Jesus. The original version was of a pelican piercing its breast, but over the centuries the bird has become symbolic, and certainly this one, from Gessner's *Natural History* (1555), bears little resemblance to a pelican.

and its emblematic and moral significance—and precious little about its physiology and ecology.

Only with the advent of the scientific revolution in the middle of the seventeenth century did this begin to change. The philosopher Henry More (1614–1687) for example, delighted in exposing the fallacy of folklore. At that time it was widely believed that a dead kingfisher suspended from a silk thread would point its beak in the direction of approaching weather. By holding up two kingfishers simultaneously, or the same bird twice in succession, Henry More showed how the beaks rarely pointed in the same direction, and hence exposed the naïve nature of such beliefs.

John Ray (1627–1705), arguably the greatest naturalist that ever lived and another pioneer of the scientific revolution, introduced the idea of physico-theology in his book *The Wisdom of God manifested in the Works of the Creation*, published in 1691. He promoted the idea that the extraordinary match between an animal's design or behaviour and its environment—what today we'd call an adaptation—was the result of the Creator's wisdom. Not only that, Ray said that God had provided the natural world for man's enjoyment and education, and in this sense Ray is the father of field natural history. Prior to John Ray people were God-fearing; Ray gave them a different and much more positive perspective. The idea of physico-theology was popular, not least because Ray was an excellent writer and a perceptive naturalist (you can download *The Wisdom of God* for free, and once you've got used to the 'olde-worlde' language, it is a fascinating read). So successful was physico-theology that it became the basis for the clergyman-as-naturalist—epitomised by Gilbert White (1720–1793), author of *The Natural History of Selborne*.

William Paley borrowed (some say stole) Ray's idea to produce his own book, *Natural Theology*, 1802, to make the same points and to use natural history to promote Christian beliefs. Paley's book was recommended reading for those at Cambridge—like Charles Darwin —thinking about going into the church. Darwin was fascinated by the notion of adaptation, but once he developed the idea of natural selection in the 1830s he realised that this provided a much more compelling explanation for the natural world than natural theology. He set out his ideas for the first time in the *Origin of the Species,* which was published in 1859.

Darwin's explanation for the natural world is now widely recognised as being correct, certainly in Britain and elsewhere in Europe, and natural selection is the foundation upon which all modern biology now occurs. As the biologist Theodosius Dobzhansky said: "Nothing in biology makes sense except in the light of evolution".

Those who enjoy natural history refer to themselves as naturalists, or natural historians. Natural history is, as we have seen, based on science, although most of those that call themselves naturalists adopt an observational rather than experimental approach. However, many of today's professional biologists started out as young naturalists.

Natural history is in a precarious state today, partly because children are prevented from discovering the natural world for themselves. Many young people grow up in a world where their main exposure to natural history occurs via television. Of course programmes like those written and presented by Sir David Attenborough are excellent, but they are no substitute for finding things out for oneself. The lack of direct experience of the natural world is very evident among young people entering university to read biology: rarely do they know the difference between an oak and an alder, a blackbird and blackcap or a stoat and squirrel. Many of their teachers, born in the 1940s, 1950s and 1960s, were inspired to become professional biologists and researchers through natural history, and through their own discovery of natural history by watching birds, and by collecting beetles or wildflowers. Ask any of this previous generation of biology teachers what inspired them and it will often be some kind of epiphany where they saw something, or discovered something, for themselves. Hoping for an epiphany through watching television, is a bit like hoping that a peck on the cheek from a lover will be as meaningful as a kiss on the lips.

To rectify this dismal state of affairs we need to ensure that the next generation of children are allowed direct access to the natural world (or what's left of it). Certainly guidance from teachers is important, but there is really no substitute for the real thing. In a sense, children are the hope for the future. We need a new generation to be inspired by nature, because we need them to protect it—for their children. It sounds trite, but it is true.

See: Adaptation, Epiphany.

Natural selection

This is the process by which particular forms of organisms that are best adapted to a particular environment increase in numbers over time, compared with less well-adapted forms.

See: Adaptation.

Nature writing

Nature writing: a literary genre; a publishing enterprise; and, a growth area for recruitment to university postgraduate creative writing classes.

This grove of literary culture has prospered of late, flowering thanks to the creative energies of a bunch of influential practitioners, and the judicious application of a label of 'newness'; see for example the

Granta magazine of 2008. Commercial success, critical acclaim, and the polite communities of the summer book festival circuit have lent public profile to leading talents. So much so that open season has recently been declared (see Jonathan Bate in *The Guardian*, June 2011) on nature writing as a genre now "ripe for parody", on account of a derivative style that is too mannered, and a tone too consistently earnest for some reading tastes. The inevitable backlash duly noted, in its most poised passages, nature writing is the sort of portraiture that shifts and shimmers with life, capturing creaturely conditions, and reflecting the artist's own patterns of experience. Descriptions of natural events or tantalising encounters with otherness are taut and precise. These can be definitive enough to bring to mind images of the highest resolution, brokering understanding without recourse to clunking analysis. And yet simultaneously, these descriptions achieve the pleasing effect—one that is wholly intended—of being left ajar, as if to invite the reader's own affinitive thinking or revelatory wonder. Devin Johnston's (2009) latest essay collection shows off this effect exquisitely. Better still some of the prose entries surfacing in the *Journals* (2000) of poet, the late R. F. Langley. His notices from the ritualised, evening dog walk—crepuscular, crisp and cauterised—demand repeat reading.

Things were not always so rosy for a form of writing that takes as its subject the ordinary operations of the natural world, shaped in a language of lyrical description, born of proximal relations and the closest vigils kept, all the while eschewing scientific neutrality in favour of personal sentiment and human empathy. Across the twentieth century—as Tim Dee (2010) notes reflectively in a piece for literary journal *Archipelago*—the genre enjoyed fluctuating fortunes. Not so long ago such literature was dismissed by critics with a metropolitan caste of mind for inhabiting a pastoral or provincial "thoughtworld", and from time to time for the expression of socially conservative values. If nature writing has now come of age, then arguably this is because it reflects the troubled temper of our times. Love of the countryman's lore, a passion for gentle accounts of topographical touring and an appreciation of most careful renderings of animal, bird and plant life remain durable topics, afforded added currency in an age characterised by mounting public concern about the plight of the environment. Anxiety about irreversible local change is in itself nothing new, but is amplified when placed in a context of resource depletion, habitat destruction, the diminution of biodiversity, atmospheric warming and significant environmental change on a global scale. That this wide-lens world, brimful of the harshest facts, might slip by without any explicit mention in the nature writer's notes matters not one jot. A background awareness of the damage already done on planet earth is what haunts today's environmental imagination, compelling the readers' urge for escape, stirring their desire to be re-enchanted or to have the palette cleansed of bitter pollutants.

Practitioners of nature writing are well-read, bookish sorts—several notables earned their stripes as students of English Literature—who claim equal appeal in the library shelf and a life spent in the open air. Readers in Britain, of the armchair kind or out-and-about sort, seem among the keenest to be affected, and not just by today's writers either, but as willing explorers of a rich heritage of long-forgotten local voices and overlooked regional prose. Interesting moves are afoot in places abroad from these islands too. The deepening and broadening of public literacy in landscape is a project that now falls within the compass of efforts to envision an alternative America; one where the environment is not simply treated as a dirty word, badly compromised by corporate science or deployed as a political tool for greater economic leverage. Marshalled by Barry Lopez (2006), the *Home Ground* nature writing collective stake out a better and richer social future, one that taps into a great well-spring of vernacular knowledge about the United States' diversity of terrains and topographic features. The digest of knowledge assembled gives voice to oral traditions, ones often first spoken by indigenous peoples, in languages and dialects that name scenic features by telling their stories. In so doing they demonstrate a shared respect for older, sagebrush wisdoms.

Where might the experimental naturalist, or seeker of new sights, turn for their literary kicks nowadays? That quest begins in the compromised, estuarine, heavily populated kinds of place where Robert Macfarlane's (2008) notable search for vestigial kinds of wildness left off. Humbled and hobbled, new veins of writing are bearing witness to that which exists *after* nature. This work chronicles tender beauties in the most botched or malignant of forms, finds qualities of character in the cruellest and bloodiest of acts, compiles field-notes about the feral finds made in contaminated dross-scapes, and charts picturesque routes through post-industrial edgelands. Announced by the arrival of writers more avowedly angry and angular than their forebears, these ventures suggest the formulation of an alternative environmental aesthetic, written in a seething, scabrous spirit, that is dissenting and knowingly contrary. Evading the age-old fear of nature deficit, detachment or estrangement, their preferred conduct is to come upon worlds that have passed over the threshold, proliferating in already disfigured states. Their craft, to pen words offering no immediate comfort, little in the way of consolation, and that instead document the dread of a felt world in a time of reckoning.

See: Epiphany, Liminal zone, Natural history.

Palliative curation

Lord Braybroke constructed the lighthouse at Orford Ness in 1792 to guide ships through treacherous shingle banks off the Suffolk coast. The light is still operational, but Trinity House is in the process of decommisioning it, which will involve removing hazardous materials such as the mercury in the lamp. This follows a review which found that the lighthouse is no longer required as an aid to navigation. Trinity House has entered into discussions with the National Trust about transferring ownership of the lighthouse. Every year the sea shaves off another section of shingle spit, and the base of the lighthouse is now

Orford Ness lighthouse

less than twenty metres from the beach crest. The Trust is weighing up the implications of taking on a 220 year-old building in a precarious location. If and when the transfer of ownership takes place, the National Trust intends to 'let nature take its course' and allow the sea to gradually claim the structure. This sounds straightforward enough, but it's difficult to imagine how this would play out over time. Public safety concerns may well mitigate against the unmanaged collapse of the structure, and the eventual agent of destruction is more likely to be a bulldozer than rising sea swell.

Perhaps, but a slight shift in perspective may open up other possibilities. Several years ago a friend of mine in Montana coined the term 'palliative curation' to refer to the philosophy we'd adopted in managing elements of a derelict homestead site. Many of the structures were too far gone to preserve, even in a state of arrested decay, but instead of demolishing them we decided to let them gradually disintegrate; we would document their transformation attentively, with respect for their past and curiosity about their future. This morning, as I was thinking about writing this entry, BBC Radio 4 interviewed Rob George, a palliative care consultant, about the findings of an independent review into end-of-life care in the UK. He explained that the aim of palliative care is to "help people cope with uncertainty—in the movement between life and death". While obviously of a different order and intensity, a similar sense of uncertainty characterises our relationships with cultural artefacts that have a finite (if indeterminate) lifespan. The tendency is to look away, and pretend that all is well, until the expiration date arrives. An ethic of palliative curation suggests other ways of approaching this interval of uncertainty—creating opportunities to say 'goodbye' to loved landmarks and landscapes, and allow them to die with dignity. At Orford Ness, this could involve the careful monitoring of the lighthouse's disintegration, with an attempt made to salvage architectural features and incorporate them into new structures. The gradual stages of unmaking could be accompanied by cultural events, rituals of leave-taking that help us bridge the gap between 'there' and 'gone'.

See: Aspic, Entropy, Managed realignment.

Place

If memory and anticipation are two sides of the same coin, one pointing backward, the other facing forward, then place might be thought of as the edge that runs around the coin in an infinite loop, always connecting the two but simultaneously keeping them distinct.

As the pause between past and future, *place* always functions in, from, and through the present. It depends on apprehension for its own instantiation; with every effort to encounter, to understand, to attribute meaning, we make place anew. And yet, paradoxically, one of the key characteristics of place is the way that it affords a sense of persistence, rootedness, stasis and fixity.

See: Memory.

Presentism

We make our stories about the past; we don't find them fully formed. But some makings are purer and more acceptable than others. Undergraduate teaching of history inevitably includes a discussion of 'presentism'—a trap for the unwary or unscrupulous historian whose assembly of historical data works (intentionally or not) to legitimate a present point of view. When the unavoidable necessity of selection shades into the possibility of deliberate manipulation, that way madness lies. George Stocking catalogued the sins of presentism as follows: "anachronism, distortion, misleading analogy, neglect of context, oversimplification of process". But perhaps things are bit murkier than they were in 1965 when Stocking compiled this list? We now introduce the concept of presentism alongside other key terms that include pluralism, positionality, reflexivity, and situated knowledge. Are the sins of presentism still so relevant in a relativist era? Do we have any chance of transcending our present point of view when we approach the making of history, and should we be pretending to?

Maybe we need to go even further and embrace the possibility of a 'futurist' history? The Futurist movement's engagement with the ideas of Henri Bergson provides some context for what such a history might look like. Bergson's theory of time and human experience focused on the perception of a dynamic world, a world defined by matter in flux and universal 'becoming'.

> This reality is mobility. Not things made, but things in the making, not self maintaining states, but only changing states, exist. Rest is never more than apparent, or, rather, relative.

He wrote about the human body as a "moving boundary between the future and the past", and was interested in the perceived simultaneity of memory traces, present experience, and the anticipation of future events. A form of history influenced by these ideas may be oddly appropriate in this moment, especially if it could set the temporal complexity of landscape perception (where the past is always present) against a background context of environmental change.

See: Equilibrium, Futurology, Memory.

Record

A document that is intended to store and communicate evidence about the past. In terms of the documentation of historic environments, landscapes and natures, there exists an almost unimaginably large archive of paper records. These in turn come in a bewildering array of styles and formats, including personal diaries documenting seasonal changes in nature; correspondence between naturalists; instrumental records of daily weather; maps of land-use and topography; and published material in the shape of newspaper reports, magazines and books. There are also records in the shape of specimens taken from nature. These might include dried and pressed plants; seeds; minerals; soil samples; mounted insects; a tree ring; or an ice core. Then there are the records that advances in technology made possible in the twentieth century. The BBC, for instance, established

Ludwig Koch field recording.

its sound archive in 1936 and its recordings date back to the late nineteenth century. Included in its archive are recordings of bird song, captured by Ludwig Koch and Max Nicholson in the 1930s. Natural history programmes are now a staple on our television screens and increasingly present one of the most important mediums through which people establish an emotional relationship with nature. There are notable repositories of nature's archives that come in the shape of natural history museums, such as Kew Gardens or the Natural History Museum, both in London, where one can find seeds, bones, and stuffed animals alongside paper records, sound and video recordings and digital information. These institutions have long styled themselves as arks—as the encompassment of the entirety of God's nature under one roof. That term is still used today, but with a different end in mind—the preservation of nature's diversity in the face of systematic extermination at the hands of humans.

See: Extinction, Museum, Recording.

Recording

Humans have been recording their observations of nature for millennia. Aristotle was doing so as far back as the fourth century BC. In fact his books on natural history were still widely consulted up to the Renaissance. However, received ideas about what to include in these accounts—in terms of the sort of information that was appropriate and the sort of creatures that should be present—were gradually overturned. One of the main reasons for this was the importation into Europe of a new body of animals and plants from the various voyages of exploration taking place at that time. Exotic animals from far-flung parts of the world highlighted the parochialism of supposedly exhaustive European bestiaries. It was also impossible to produce accounts of these creatures along established lines—how could one write about an animal's place in fables and folklore, for instance, when for all intents and purposes it had only just come into existence? Consequently, the recording of natural history gradually took on a more observational approach, focusing on description and anatomical investigation. The incorporation of visual imagery helped this along and was genuinely revolutionary—the classic works of natural history by the likes of Aristotle, Pliny, Albertus and Aelianus contained virtually no illustrations of the animals under discussion.

This observational approach to the recording of nature was facili-tated by the scientific revolution in the sixteenth and seventeenth centuries, which placed great store on first-hand experience, the efficacy of mathematics as the language of nature, and the value of instrumental accounts. In Britain alone there was an explosion of accounts of the island's nature, helped of course by improvements in printing technologies. There were descriptions of nature at a variety of scales. Gilbert White produced a record of nature in his own parish of Selborne—*The Natural History of Selborne*, published in 1789. There was a rash of county-level studies, exemplified by Robert Plot's *Natural History of Oxfordshire*, published in 1677. There were also numerous national natural histories, although these tended, given their size, to restrict themselves in their scope. Science became increasingly popular

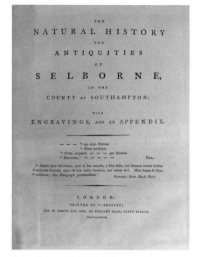

First edition of White's *Selborne*, 1789.

in the late eighteenth century and cheap books of identification for budding naturalists were published. Many of these books provided space under the names of species where users could record their own comments and observations, a remark pertaining perhaps to the location of the found object, to the weather or the season. As the historian Anne Secord has noted, these books were designed not only to encourage their owners to keep records, but also to shape their way of seeing by underlining the importance of scientific arrangement.

The explosion of scientific societies in the Victorian era also encouraged people to go out and observe and record their local nature. Most of these societies produced their own reports and transactions, and they were stuffed with lists of newly found plants, animals, minerals, and antiquities, records of folktales, and weather records. These records remain integral to today's efforts to reconstruct environment change over time, whether in terms of rates of precipitation, extinctions, introductions or habitat loss. It is a sad fact that in the main these societies have come to the end of their natural lives. However, the recording of nature remains a popular past-time. The RSPB's annual Big Garden Birdwatch encourages so-called 'citizen scientists' to monitor and record the changing fortunes of birds and other garden wildlife, while the success of television programmes such as the BBC's Springwatch illustrate just how popular the daily observation of nature still is. Amateur weather stations also increasingly feed their data into national repositories such as the UK's Met Office, even if these larger bodies can be wary of these stations due to uncertainties about the reliability and placement of their instruments and the accuracy of their data.

Another shift in what we might call the culture of recording is the almost ubiquitous use of computer software to do what a journal or diary would have done only 30 years ago. Until fairly recently, an assiduous naturalist who came across the tracks of an otter would have written a letter to their local wildlife trust, detailing when and where they had seen this. Today this is all done using electronic databases, where the information is limited to species name, date, grid reference, location name, number, sex, record type and observer. The ability to share records amongst regional organisations using online tools like the National Biodiversity Network is a significant benefit to those who want to track the changing fortunes of nature across nations. However, for the historian of natural history, the opportunities that computers open up are offset by risks. Paper records tend to contain a lot more information than their online equivalents, whether in terms of the relationship between the writer and the receiver, the recorder's fieldwork practices, their wider views on nature or even what they had for breakfast. So for every valuable online record there is an attendant loss of information. And that is not to mention the loss of paper archives that are increasingly deemed irrelevant or just simply too expensive to store.

See: Introductions, Monitoring; Natural history, Record.

Rewilding

In December 1939 the Government Code and Cypher School constructed a rectangular, timber-framed building at Bletchley Park to house the operations of a special unit tasked with intercepting and deciphering German Army and Air Force encrypted Enigma traffic. Seventy years later I visited the site with a research team and found Hut 6 in an advanced state of dereliction (right). A healthy sycamore sapling had rooted in the hut's rusty guttering. A thriving community of stonecrop strung out along the gutter's length, an aerial garden tended by benign neglect. In other parts of the site, windowsills sprouted tiny grasslands, ivy clambered through open windows, and moss formed thick roof-blankets. While some areas in the extensive Bletchley Park complex had been restored and adapted for reuse, the places that had been left to their own devices were gradually rewilding. Recombinant ecologies exposed the vulnerability of the structures against an invasion of relict prewar plants and more recent interlopers. The vegetation acted as a living clock for measuring the time elapsed since intensive regimes of wartime maintenance gave way to an interval of invisibility, and then a more recent episode of under-funded heritage reclamation. Shortly after I visited the site, the Bletchley Park Trust received £250,000 for urgent repairs to the 'at-risk code-breaking buildings', and a decision on an additional £4 million in Heritage Lottery Funding is due this year. Bletchley's rewilding will be reversed, the primacy of the cultural reasserted over the natural. But that may be too simple a formulation. In other residual military landscapes—Hanford Reach National Monument, Rocky Flats National Wildlife Refuge—rewilding is deliberately (if not necessarily cynically) enlisted in what David Havlick calls 'military-to-wildlife conversions'. Here, ecological processes can become cultural agents of attempted historical erasure, and naturalisation risks negation.

See: Entropy, Palliative curation, Story-radar.

Rhododendron

Rhododendron is a genus of flowering plants found primarily in the northern hemisphere—in the Mediterranean and eastwards through Asia into China. Introduced to Britain in the late eighteenth century, rhododendrons were a popular addition to country estates in the Victorian period, where they provided cover for game birds in addition to their ornamental and aesthetic value. The botanist and plant collector Joseph Dalton Hooker added about 25 new rhododendron species to the 50 already known during his expedition to India and Nepal in 1849–51 and the new species helped create something of a 'rhododendron craze' amongst British gardeners.

Rhododendrons have been able to out-compete many native plants in Britain, and because their leaves are inedible to many animals, their spread has proved difficult to control and they have become reclassified as pests. They grow to great heights, allowing very little light to penetrate their thick leaf canopy.

The Forestry Commission now offer Woodland Improvement Grants for rhododendron removal in Cornwall, Devon and Exmoor following a number of outbreaks of *Phytophthora ramorum* (Sudden Oak Death). Rhododendron is a host of this parasite, which represents a serious threat to the survival of the region's ancient and native woodlands. Among those plants being burned on official orders are treasured 150 year old rhododendrons at the Lost Gardens of Heligan.

Honey made from rhododendron nectar can cause hallucinations, loss of co-ordination and vertigo.

See: Acclimatisation, Introductions, Woods.

Sculpture trail, 26 April 2011. *Left to right, top to bottom:* 1. Towards Rosewall Hill; 2. Rosewall summit; 3. Mine engine ruins; 4. Footpath; 5. Map; 6. Gate; 7. Stile; 8. Gorse path; 9. The west face of Rosewall; 10. National Trust gateway to Trevalgan.

Sculpture trail

"I, the sculptor, am the landscape. I am the form and I am the hollow, the thrust and the contour."

In 1952 Barbara Hepworth said that she "gradually discovered the remarkable pagan landscape which lies between St. Ives, Penzance and Land's End; a landscape which still has a deep effect on me" (quoted

Barbara Hepworth drawing on Rosewall, above St Ives, from *A Pictorial Autobiography*, 1970.

in Read's *Barbara Hepworth*). This specific topography acted as both inspiration and subject for her modernist sculptures. Strangely, for an artist so engaged with her local landscape, only a very few of her works are named after specific places. This rarity of place-name titling imbues those sites she did entitle with a particular sense of significance.

The photographs (above, p.63) are from a larger sequence that sets out to document a walk taken between Hepworth's sculpture, 'Rosewall' to another, 'Trevalgan'—a sculpture trail. ('Rosewall', Nebrasina stone, 1960–62, is now located in Chesterfield; 'Trevalgan', bronze, 1956, six editions are now housed around Europe and the USA.)

The photographs present West Penwith as a wild and rural place, exposed to harsh Atlantic weather fronts, where bronze age menhirs sit alongside the stone ruins and engine houses of the region's more recent mining past, as well as National Trust signage, rickety stiles, rambling hikers and picnicking tourists. The images disclose the palimpsestic landscape. Traces of Hepworth's 'pagan' landscape remain alongside other landscapes from the past and the present: agricultural, post-industrial, tourist, and pre-historic.

See: Art, Moor.

Shifting baseline syndrome

At Mullion Harbour, on the Lizard peninsula, growing maintenance costs, rising sea levels and increasing storm intensity led to a 2006 decision to initiate decommissioning and deconstruction of the 116 year-old harbour walls "at an unpredictable point in the near or distant future". Justin Whitehouse, National Trust Head Ranger, sent this email to Caitlin DeSilvey in response to a draft anticipatory history of the harbour:

"…I am often reminded of 'shifting baseline syndrome' when it comes to trying to explain the concept of change. What people perceive to be either natural or desirable (or permanent in the case of the harbour) is restricted by their personal and 'generational' amnesia, due to relatively short life spans and memories. Used mainly to describe changes in nature and landscapes, the concept is just as relevant to the built environment. No one remembers Mullion without a harbour (nor do they remember sea levels being almost a metre lower than today).

"The Trust hosts many school visits to the harbour where we try to explain the concept of change. When asked how old they think the harbour is, the answers vary from ten years to ten million years old! Timeless indeed. Old photos are wonderful for showing how the harbour (and the land around the harbour) has changed over the past 120 years or so. The children look how things have changed, trying to find where the old photos were taken from. I draw a timeline in the sand on the beach. At one end, 400 million years ago when the Lizard formed, through to the present day, with the various historical events marked along the line (dinosaurs, ice ages, Romans, 1066 etc). The harbour's life is a mere blip of time scratched into the sand. We then extend the timeline to 'anticipate the future'."

See: Managed realignment, Presentism, Temprocentrism.

Story-radar

The active identification of narrative threads within representations of 'fact'. William Cronon, writing in the *Journal of American History* in 1992, tells us that history is replete with "narrative swirls", which are embedded in even the most anodyne and ostensibly objective chronological accounts. Story-radar acts as a device to detect those narrative swirls. Its cultural antennae recognise the hints, gestures, and tropes of unspoken, overarching story-lines, and make visible their hidden morals and logics. Such storylines may include grand epic narratives about humanity's descent from Eden, nature's subjugation, nature's revenge, or nature's capacity to heal itself. Another familiar storyline projects a narrative of renunciation—a formula latent in debates on both sides of the political spectrum—where cars, supermarkets, large houses and air travel (all things we enjoy) should be surrendered in order to defeat climate change.

Yet another story-line is the anti-science and technology argument, framed in the short but vividly storied statement: "If god had intended us to fly he would have given us wings". This snippet distils suspicion about the causes of, and/or solutions to, climate change. Its countless derivates stymie debate and close off possibilities for action.

Aerial view of 'Cobra-Mist' radar station, Orford Ness, c.1971, and the same landscape now, re-storied as the 'Orford Ness National Nature Reserve'.

Still another is the narrative of the undeserving poor. In a peculiarly blatant reversal of the parable of the Good Samaritan, we watch on the news or read in the press about work-shy benefit cheats claiming disability allowance while they discretely pursue a life of reckless adventure—bungee jumping, jungle trekking, or mountain climbing, for example. These stories are not balanced by coverage of the 'undeserving rich'; they are shown with relish to emphasise the sensibilities of suspicion that underpin a neoliberal position.

Stories contain within them a plotted sequence in which a tension is ultimately resolved. They are satisfying and attractive and compelling precisely because they make sense. The allure of stories makes them an important political device. Election campaign literature demonstrates the huge effort involved in formulating particular stories and making them stick—opponents are liars, or are weak, or are Volvo-driving, latte-sipping, granola-eating unpatriotic liberals. That the brand of car and breakfast choice of one group of voters becomes so stereotyped is an indication of the rhetorical power of narrative.

Activist Patrick Reinsborough (smartmeme.org) recognizes this: he talks about the "battle for the story, rather than the story of the battle". We need story-radar to help us pay attention to narratives, because as Rebecca Solnit points out, "at least half of any battle turns out to be over just what the story is and who gets to tell it" (http://www.tomdispatch.com/archive/175236/).

See: Catastrophe, Futurology, Rewilding.

Temprocentrism

The tendency to take for granted the premises, expectations and values of one's own timeframe. As Robert Textor observes in *The World Ahead,* such an outlook makes it hard to "pay critical yet imaginative attention to future possibilities and probabilities, and hence harder for individuals, communities or societies to realize future opportunities and avoid future dangers". People with deeply temprocentric world-views struggle to acknowledge and accept evidence of change in their environment (for instance erosion, flooding, sea level rise). Such a condition may lead to a state of 'disownment' or denial, which shifts responsibility for mitigation and adaptation to future generations.

See: Equilibrium, Presentism.

Tides

The earth, the moon and the sun conspire through gravity to play havoc with the majority of the world's seas. We measure tides in the UK from a single benchmark known as the Chart Datum. Strangely enough in this high-tech world this common standard derives from a plaque bolted to a wall in the harbour at Newlyn, Cornwall. We classify the twice monthly tidal cycle with strange words: springs for those with the biggest range and neaps for those where the range is more contained. Tidal range varies according to geography. The extreme mega-tidal range of the Bristol Channel, with a 15m variation between high and low contrasts with those at Weymouth, just a 100 miles away as the crow flies. Here the tidal range barely exceeds the height of the average human. In the Baltic, a virtually land-locked sea, one can measure the tidal range across the span of a human hand.

Where tides do have significant range they appear to be wild and untamed, as huge volumes of water exchange every six hours, but there are rules, most particularly The Rule of Twelfths, and tides are required to play by them. The Rule of Twelfths insists that from low-water on the first hour of a rising tide one twelfth of the volume of water pushes landward. In the second hour two twelfths. In the third hour three twelfths. The fourth hour three twelfths, the fifth hour two twelfths and the sixth hour, as we head towards high tide, one twelfth. At high tide we arrive at slack water, another wonderful term describing how the tide pauses to catch its breath before observing the Law of Twelfths in reverse to empty the cistern and take us back some six hours later to low water.

Tides are on the one hand predictable, illustrated by the very precise way we can calculate and forecast how they will manifest in response to the planets. We can predict the astronomical height of a tide at any given location, years, decades and even centuries in advance. We can even hindcast tides to find out what the tide was doing on a given day in history. And yet in spite of this mathematical predictability the final extent of any tide on any given day, how high or how low, is hugely influenced by prevailing meteorological conditions. Low atmospheric pressure, often associated with stormy weather, sucks up the sea surface, allowing the tide to exceed its astronomical prediction. Often aided and abetted on these occasions by strong winds piling water onto our coasts, the astronomical prediction can be exceeded by several metres. Look out coastal towns and cities when nature synchronises itself in this way: here comes the flood. Equally, at low water on spring tides with prevailing high pressure the sea surface is pushed lower than the force exerted by gravity and on these occasions a brief glimpse of drowned landscapes is revealed.

There are so many brilliant attributes to tides. There is an 18 year cycle of enhanced gravitational push and pull resulting in bigger tidal ranges. Take a look at this on the Proudman Oceanographic Laboratory where you can see the highest and lowest predicted tides from 2006 to 2028 for any major UK port. We peak again in 2014/15. (http://www.pol.ac.uk/ntslf/tidalp.html)

A parting fact about tides is that twice a day the whole of Britain's south west peninsula experiences a wobble of around one millimetre as the tide rushes in on our coast. At high water the south west is one millimetre lower due to the weight of water on our shores than it is six hours later at low water.

See: Ebb and flood, Uncertainty.

Uncertainty

	London			Cardiff			Edinburgh			Belfast		
	High	Med	Low	High	Med	Low	High	Med	Low	High	Med	Low
2000	3.5	3.0	2.5	3.5	2.9	2.5	2.2	1.6	1.2	2.3	1.7	1.3
2010	7.3	6.2	5.3	7.3	6.2	5.3	4.7	3.5	2.6	4.9	3.8	2.8
2020	11.5	9.7	8.2	11.5	9.7	8.2	7.5	5.7	4.3	7.8	6.0	4.6
2030	16.0	13.5	11.4	15.9	13.4	11.4	10.7	8.2	6.1	11.1	8.6	6.6
2040	20.8	17.5	14.8	20.8	17.5	14.8	14.2	10.9	8.2	14.7	11.4	8.7
2050	25.8	21.8	18.4	25.9	21.8	18.4	18.0	13.9	10.5	18.6	14.5	11.1
2060	31.4	26.3	22.2	31.4	26.3	22.2	22.1	17.1	13.0	22.9	17.8	13.7
2070	37.2	31.2	26.3	37.1	31.1	26.3	26.6	20.6	15.7	27.4	21.4	16.5
2080	43.3	36.3	30.5	43.3	36.2	30.5	31.4	24.4	18.6	32.3	25.3	19.6
2090	49.7	41.6	35.0	49.7	41.6	35.0	36.5	28.4	21.8	37.6	29.4	22.8
2095	53.1	44.4	37.3	53.1	44.4	37.3	39.2	30.5	23.4	40.3	31.6	24.5

Central estimates for relative sea level changes (cm) with respect to 1990 levels, under high, medium, and low emissions scenarios. UKCIP 2009.

See: Futurology, Tides.

Unfarming

Post-industrialism doesn't feel too good if you once made a living from building cars or digging coal. And unfarming will rub what remains of farming up likewise. What remains is considerable but farming is more and more about doing less. Reduced intensity tenancies or stewardships of land held for generations, monies to be made and skylarks to be helped by set-aside, the rewetting of the Cambridge-shire fens, the farm as theme park—all are versions of unfarming. But the ugly term needs handling with care. It suggests a new wisdom but older understandings might be cleverer. Farmers cannot be kept from their farms. New top-end science also suggests further complications and far reaching decisions ahead. Biodiversity might be best maintained by abandoning some land to intensification, to the most calculated and industrialized of refarmings. Organic and apparently sustainable farming might work for rich and northern countries. But if that is all we have India will go hungry. Similarly we must be on our guard against the misreading the bourgeois good life prompts. Since its beginnings farming has been about genetic modification: captive breeding and the development of crops is how we have fed ourselves. Unfarming must be more than just agitprop.

See: Adaptation, Rewilding.

Woods

What is a wood? Trees so densely stocked as to merit a boundary line on a map? In cold terms, maybe. But there are many other ways of describing woods. They are mysterious, disorienting, sacred, quiet, noisy, full of ancient living things that were there before we were born and will outlive us. Time passes slowly for

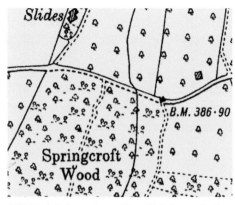

1936 6-inch Ordnance Survey Map of Ash, Sevenoaks, Kent

trees and where there are lots of them altogether, it passes very slowly indeed. And woods are not just trees—there are other kinds of wooded places such as pasture-woodlands that have been grazed by cattle, sheep, deer and pigs for centuries and sometimes thousands of years.

Woods are dynamic. Even the stunted and wind-shaped oaks in Wistman's Wood, high on Dartmoor, have changed and will change, albeit imperceptibly. Without the traumatic interference of chainsaws, axes and heavy grazing much of our countryside would become wood-land or pasture-woodland once again. Every wood, even ancient woods more than 400 years old have been used by people for gathering food, grazing animals, making charcoal, extracting timber and fuel. Now, and backalong, people valued woods for reconnecting with each other, with nature and with a supernatural world.

Some of the ways that woods change can be so traumatic as to elicit highly emotional responses. The buzz of a chainsaw followed by the snap and crash of a rain forest giant is for many the iconic image that made us want to plant a tree. In November 1987, and again in 1990, great storms swept through England bringing down tens of thousands of trees. People reacted by wanting to clear woods of dead and dying timber and replant. But these woods were not destroyed; these slowly changing woods overnight became power houses of solar energy and carbon capture, through massive natural regeneration of trees.

Understanding the changes that woods have been through over time helps us realise their significance, and can help us cope with changes too. In Johnny Wood, Borrowdale, in the Lake District, we know that the oaks which now dominate the wood are relative newcomers. Analysis of pollen deposits shows that over a few thousand years, willows gave way to hazel which gave way to alder which gave way to oak. The venerable, 'grotesque' oaks in Wistman's Wood arrived at a similarly unhurried pace.

See: Enclosure, Introductions.

Zone of exclusion

A term most associated with the 1986 Chernobyl disaster in Ukraine. A thirty kilometre zone was established around the nuclear reactor, involving the evacuation of 120,000 people from Chernobyl, Pripyat and smaller communities. The zone was subsequently reported in terms of an unplanned wildlife sanctuary (see for example, Mary Mycio's *Wormwood Forest*, significantly subtitled "a natural history of Chernobyl"). The evacuated ruins of Pripyat have become familiar through photography, and tourist visits to the zone have become more common since its depiction in computer games.

The popular fascination with Chernobyl's zone of exclusion suggests a wider cultural significance. The zone realises one persistent kind of anticipatory narrative—a world where humanity, and industrial modernity in particular, has destroyed itself. It is in many ways an attractive version of the apocalypse, with the idea of wildlife apparently flourishing in the zone. This narrative was given scientific weight by

Warning sign at the edge of Chernobyl's exclusion zone.

Sergey Gaschak's 2006 study, which suggested abundant birdlife. Møller and Mousseau's in-depth census, published in 2010, disrupted such tranquil images. Their findings suggested in fact that radiation has significantly reduced biodiversity.

This trope of an endlessly resilient and resourceful nature is common in post-apocalyptic fiction, and found an early expression in Richard Jefferies' *After London, or Wild England*, published in 1885. Jefferies' novel shows a depopulated England reclaimed by other species, with London now deserted and returned to marshland. This process of change is written with a naturalist's eye for detail, and it is this scientific precision that makes it an early ancestor of anticipatory histories. Alan Weisman's *The World Without Us* is a recent popular attempt to imagine the ecological benefits of humanity's extinction. A genealogical link with the zone of exclusion remains—Weisman developed the concept from an earlier article he wrote on the aftermath of Chernobyl.

See: Catastrophe, Discontinuity, Rewilding.

Place index

1. Alresford, Hampshire *29*
2. Bardsey Island, Gwynedd *38*
3. Belfast, Northern Ireland *69*
4. Bideford Quay, Devon *12*
5. Birling Gap, East Sussex *15, 24, 39*
6. Bletchley Park, Buckinghamshire *61*
7. Breckland, Norfolk *26*
8. Bridgwater Bay, Somerset *43*
9. Bristol Channel *67*
10. Cardiff, Wales *69*
11. Cotehele, Cornwall *35*
12. Didcot, Oxfordshire *43*
13. Dungeness, Kent *44*
14. Edinburgh, Scotland *69*
15. Formby, Mersyside *26, 40*
16. Gwennap Head, Cornwall *11*
17. Gwithian, Cornwall *25*
18. Hackney, London *44*
19. Haslemere, Surrey *50*
20. Ireland *41*
21. Johnny Wood, Borrowdale, Cumbria *70*
22. Kew Gardens, Surrey *59*
23. Kinder Scout, Derbyshire *49*
24. Lavenham, Suffolk *51*
25. Lewes, East Sussex *23*
26. London, England *69, 71*
27. Lost Gardens of Heligan, Cornwall *62*
28. Lundy Island, Devon *12*
29. Mullion Harbour, Cornwall *64–65*
30. Newlyn, Cornwall *67*
31. Orford Ness, Suffolk *56–57*
32. Pembrokeshire National Park *11*
33. Pwll Du Bay, Gower *39*
34. Selborne, Hampshire *60*
35. Sevenoaks, Kent *70*
36. Shifnal, Shropshire *31*
37. Studland, Dorset *28*
38. The Wash, East Anglia *46*
39. West Penwith, Cornwall *12–15, 32, 36, 45, 49, 63–64*
40. Weymouth, Dorset *67*
41. Wistman's Wood, Dartmoor, Devon *70*
42. Wytham Wood, Oxfordshire *47*

Contributors

Tim Birkhead
Adaptation, Epiphany, Natural history, Natural selection

David Bullock
Woods

Chris Caseldine
Continuities, Discontinuity, Entropy, Equilibrium

Stephen Daniels
Liminal zone

Tim Dee
Birds, Introductions, Managed realignment, Unfarming

Caitlin DeSilvey
Aspic, Palliative curation, Presentism, Rewilding, Uncertainty

Phil Dyke
Besanded, Coastal squeeze, Erosion, Temprocentrism, Tides

Tom Freshwater
Art

Toby Goaman-Dodson
Dream-map, Zone of exclusion

Gareth Hoskins
Catastrophe, Memory, Place, Story-radar

Alex Hunt
Futurology, Longue durée

Hayden Lorimer
Extinction, Nature writing

David Matless
Cycle of erosion, Ebb and flood

Simon Naylor
Commons, Enclosure, Monitoring, Moor, Museum, Record, Recording

Shaun Pimlott
Sculpture trail

Colin Sackett
Collection

Lucy Veale
Acclimatisation, Rhododendron

Justin Whitehouse
Shifting baseline syndrome

Victoria Whitehouse
Living landscapes

Credits

Barbara Hepworth Estate, p.64; Bluesky International Limited, p.45; Andrew Brockbank, National Trust, p.26; Caitlin DeSilvey, p.14 below, p.28, p.39, p.61; Peter Facey/Creative Commons Licence, p.29 above; Historic Environment, Cornwall Council, p.14 above, p.36; Grant Lohoar, National Trust, p.56; C.R. Markham, *Travels in Peru and India*. (London: John Murray, 1862), p.21; David Matless, p.35, cover; Shaun Pimlott, p.63; Gordon Roberts, p.40; Colin Sackett, p.29 below, p.50; Shropshire Archives, p.31; Nicholas Sinclair, p.23; Justin Whitehouse, p.65.

Acknowledgements

The Anticipatory Histories of Landscape and Wildlife network was funded by the Arts and Humanities Research Council, and brought together voices from inside and outside academia, in partnership with the National Trust. We had participation from artists, biological recorders, museum curators, radio producers, film makers, conservation professionals, and local government officials. This book is the outcome of those conversations, and hopefully captures some of their diversity and energy.

Chris Caseldine, Tim Cooper, Caitlin DeSilvey, Toby Goaman-Dodson, Mark Goldthorpe, Simon Naylor—University of Exeter.

Jon Brookes, David Bullock, Phil Dyke, Tom Freshwater, Alex Hunt, Hannah Jones, Joe Lawrence, Justin Whitehouse, Ian Wright—National Trust.

Stephen Daniels, David Matless, Lucy Veale—University of Nottingham.

Ian Bennallick—Cornwall Botanical Group; Tim Birkhead—University of Sheffield; Sara Chambers—Royal Cornwall Museum; Steve Crummay—Cornwall Council; Tim Dee—BBC; Gareth Hoskins—University of Aberystwyth; Gary Lewis—ERCCIS; Hayden Lorimer—University of Glasgow; Misha Myers—University College Falmouth-Dartington; Shaun Pimlott; Colin Sackett; Wesley Smyth—Natural England; Stella Turk; Victoria Whitehouse—Cornwall Wildlife Trust.